Holt Spanish Level 1

¡Ven conmigo!®

Grammar and Vocabulary Workbook

HOLT, RINEHART AND WINSTON
Harcourt Brace & Company
Austin • New York • Orlando • Atlanta • San Francisco • Boston • Dallas • Toronto • London

Cover Photo/Illustration Credits:
Illustration: Eva Vagretti Cockrille

Printed in the United States of America

ISBN 0–03–052678–7

25 1409 12

4500361044

Contents

CAPÍTULO 1

Nombre ________ Clase ________ Fecha ________

¡Mucho gusto!

PRIMER PASO

To say hello and goodbye, to introduce people, and to ask how someone is, you'll need to use greetings and other courtesy expressions. You'll also need to use the subject pronouns **tú** and **yo**.

ASÍ SE DICE Greetings *Pupil's Edition, p. 21*

1 Chen is spending a semester at a high school in Mexico. How would Chen respond to each of the following expressions? Write an appropriate answer for each one.

1. Buenos días, Chen. ________
2. Hasta luego. ________
3. Adiós. ________
4. Tengo que irme. ________
5. Bueno, tengo clase. ________

ASÍ SE DICE Introducing people *Pupil's Edition, p. 22*

2 During Chen's semester at the Mexican high school, he meets many new students. Use the words in the word box to complete his dialogue with Raimundo, a fellow student.

amiga	soy	amigo	se	amigos
gusto	llamas	llamo	igualmente	

RAIMUNDO ¿Y tú? ¿Cómo te (1) ________?

CHEN Me (2) ________ Chen.

RAIMUNDO (3) ________ Raimundo Gutiérrez. Éstos son mis (4) ________. Éste es mi (5) ________ Pablo. Ésta es mi (6) ________ Raquel.

CHEN ¡Mucho (7) ________!

RAQUEL (8) ________.

Nota Gramatical Spanish punctuation *Pupil's Edition, p. 23*

- Notice the upside down punctuation marks in Spanish.

  ¿Cómo te llamas? ¡Mucho gusto!
- In Spanish, an accent mark is sometimes used over vowels **(á, é, í, ó, ú)** to show which syllable in a word is stressed. The letter **ñ** has a tilde (~) over it to show that it is pronounced like the *ny* in the word *canyon*.

3 Paulette forgot to put in punctuation in her Spanish homework. Change the following sentences to questions **(Q)** or exclamations **(E)** using the correct punctuation.

1. (E) _____ Hola _____
2. (Q) _____ Hay una carta para mí
3. (E) _____ Yo soy Francisco _____
4. (Q) _____ Y tú _____
5. _____(Q) _____ Qué tal_____

4 Paulette also forgot to include accents in her assignment! Help her out by rewriting the following words using accents for the vowel in the stressed syllable. *Hint:* The stressed syllable is indicated by bold-faced letters.

MODELO at**un** = **atún**
como = **cómo**

1. Ve**ro**nica _______________
2. Benja**min** _______________
3. per**don** _______________
4. vio**lin** _______________
5. **mas**cara _______________
6. **lam**para _______________
7. te**le**fono _______________
8. heli**cop**tero _______________
9. veinti**dos** _______________
10. **a**guila _______________

5 Read the following dialogue between Maureen, Greg, and Denise and rewrite all of the words with missing accents and punctuation marks. *Hint:* There are 6 accents missing. You'll need to mark your paper 8 times.

MAUREEN Hola. _______________

GREG Buenos dias. _______________

MAUREEN Esta es mi amiga Denise. _______________

GREG Mucho gusto!, Denise. _______________

DENISE Encantada. Eh, perdon. Como te llamas tu? _______________

GREG Me llamo Greg. _______________

MAUREEN Bueno, tengo clase. Tengo que irme. _______________

GREG Hasta luego, Maureen. _______________

MAUREEN Adios. _______________

ASÍ SE DICE Greetings *Pupil's Edition, p. 24*

6 Berta loves creating crossword puzzles! Can you solve her latest puzzle?

Horizontales *(Across)*

3. Yo ______ .
4. ¿Cómo ______?
6. ______ mal.
7. Excelente = ______ .

Verticales *(Down)*

1. ¿ ______ tal?
2. Estoy ______ bien, gracias.
4. ______ bien.
5. Más o ______ .

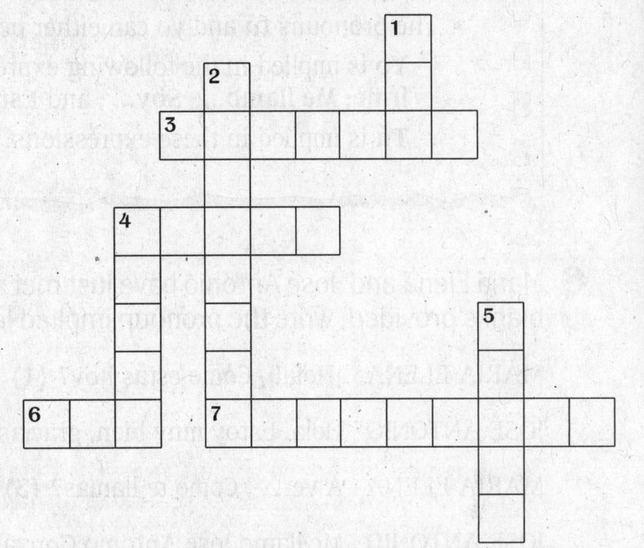

7 What question or statement would correspond to each of the following items? Remember to punctuate correctly.

1.

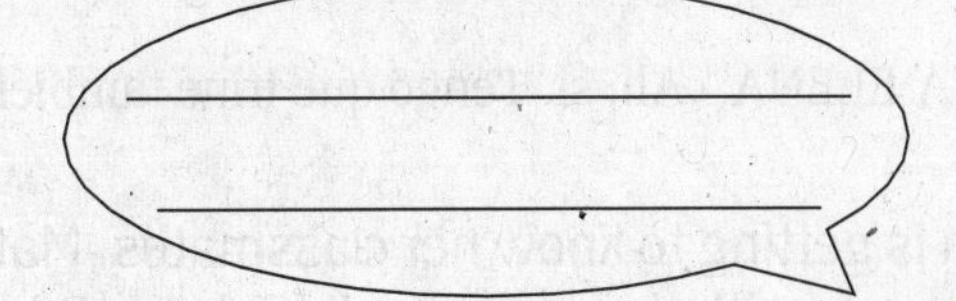

2.

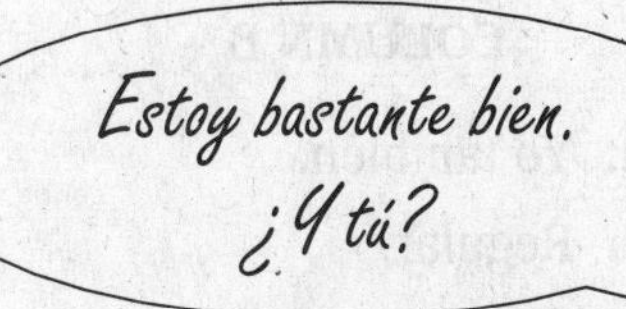

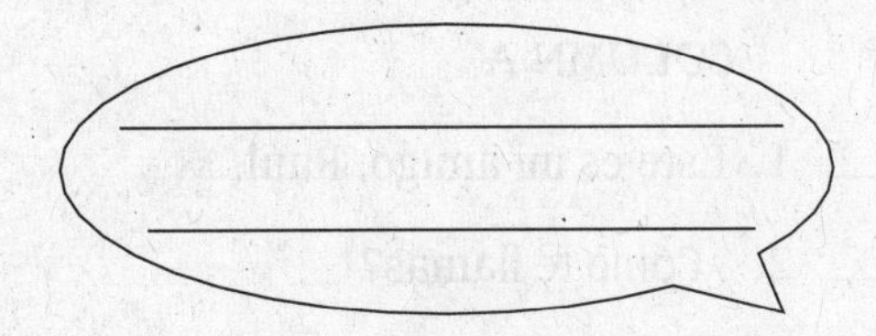

3.

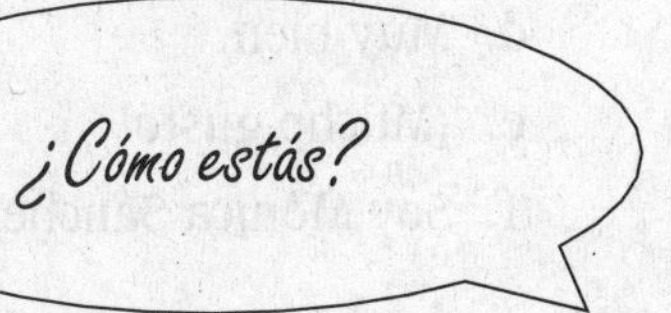

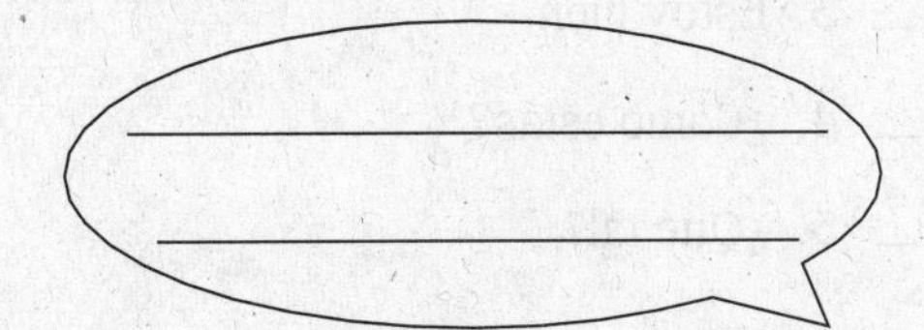

4.

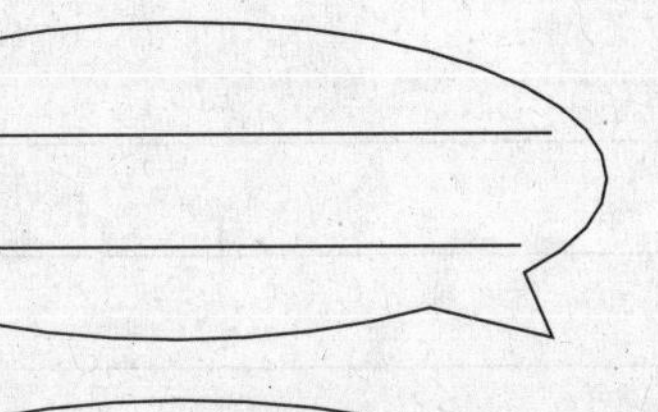

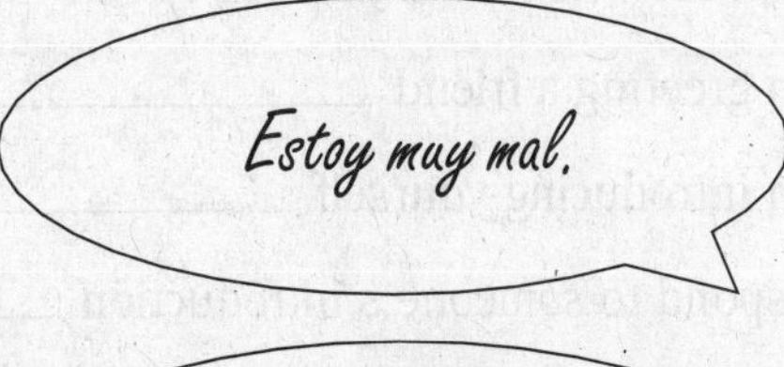

5.

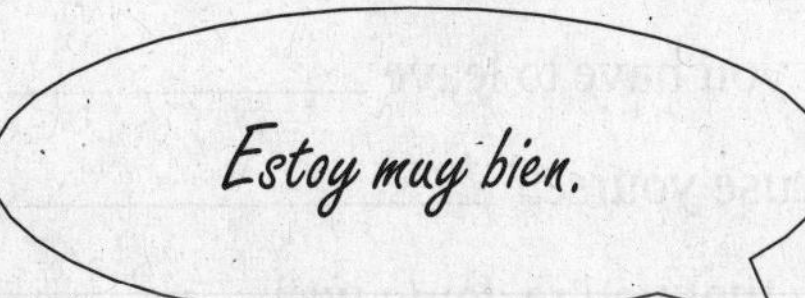

Gramática Subject pronouns tú and yo *Pupil's Edition, p. 25*

- The pronoun **yo**, capitalized only at the beginning of a sentence, is used when you refer to yourself: **Yo soy Mariela.**
- The pronoun **tú** is used when you are talking to a friend or a classmate. **¿Y tú?**
- The pronouns **tú** and **yo** can either be stated or implied.

  Yo is implied in the following expressions: **Bueno, tengo clase; Tengo que irme; Me llamo... ; Soy... ;** and **Estoy bien, gracias.**

  Tú is implied in these expressions: **¿Cómo te llamas?** and **¿Cómo estás?**

8 María Elena and José Antonio have just met at school. Read their conversation and, in the blanks provided, write the pronoun implied in each exchange.

MARÍA ELENA ¡Hola! ¿Cómo estás hoy? (1) ______________

JOSÉ ANTONIO Hola. Estoy muy bien, gracias. (2) ______________

MARÍA ELENA A ver... ¿Cómo te llamas? (3) ______________

JOSÉ ANTONIO Me llamo José Antonio González. (4) ______________

MARÍA ELENA Soy María Elena Ramírez. Mucho gusto. (5) ______________

JOSÉ ANTONIO Igualmente. ¡Uf! Tengo clase ahora. (6) ______________

MARÍA ELENA Ah, sí. Tengo que irme también. Hasta mañana, ¿eh? (7) ______________

9 Vivián is getting to know her classmates. Match each of her questions in Column A and statements with the response in Column B her classmates give.

COLUMN A	COLUMN B
_____ 1. Éste es mi amigo, Raúl.	a. Yo también.
_____ 2. ¿Cómo te llamas?	b. Regular.
_____ 3. Estoy bien.	c. Se llama Francisco.
_____ 4. ¿Cómo estás?	d. Muy bien.
_____ 5. ¿Qué tal?	e. ¡Mucho gusto!
	f. Soy Mónica Sánchez.

10 What expressions would you use . . . ?

1. when greeting a friend ______________________
2. when introducing yourself ______________________
3. to respond to someone's introduction ______________________
4. when you have to leave ______________________
5. to excuse yourself ______________________
6. to say that you're doing well ______________________

SEGUNDO PASO

To say how old someone is, you'll need to use the numbers from 0 to 30. To ask where someone is from, you'll need to use the verb **ser** and to be able to form a question.

VOCABULARIO Numbers from 0 to 30 *Pupil's Edition, p. 27*

11 Simón is working in the school bookstore taking orders for yearbooks over the phone. For each number of yearbooks ordered, write the correct numeral.

1. cinco ____________
2. diez ____________
3. veintiuno ____________
4. ocho ____________
5. siete ____________
6. treinta ____________
7. dieciocho ____________
8. quince ____________
9. veintiséis ____________
10. trece ____________

12 Simón's boss wants to know how many yearbooks have been ordered by each customer. Help Simón by writing the following numbers in Spanish words.

1. 8 ____________
2. 2 ____________
3. 12 ____________
4. 20 ____________
5. 16 ____________
6. 22 ____________
7. 26 ____________
8. 17 ____________
9. 4 ____________
10. 30 ____________

13 Claudia needs help with her math problems. Help her solve these math problems by filling in the blanks with the correct words.

MODELO 2 + 3 = **dos** y **tres** son **cinco**

1. 4 + 5 = ____________ y ____________ son ____________
2. 11 + 10 = ____________ y ____________ son ____________
3. 20 + 8 = ____________ y ____________ son ____________
4. 16 + 2 = ____________ y ____________ son ____________
5. 5 + 24 = ____________ y ____________ son ____________
6. 12 + 14 = ____________ y ____________ son ____________
7. 13 + 16 = ____________ y ____________ son ____________
8. 27 + 2 = ____________ y ____________ son ____________
9. 7 + 4 = ____________ y ____________ son ____________
10. 1 + 9 = ____________ y ____________ son ____________

Nota Gramatical The verb ser *Pupil's Edition, p. 28*

You use the verb **ser** to say where someone is from.

- To describe where you are from, you would say:

  (Yo) soy de....

- To ask a friend where he or she is from, you might say:

  ¿De dónde eres (tú)?

- To ask where someone else is from, you might say:

  ¿De dónde es Ana?

14 At an international youth conference, you overhear people telling where they're from. Fill in each blank with the correct form of **ser.**

1. Yo ____________ de San Francisco, California.
2. Miguel ____________ de Madrid.
3. ¿De dónde ____________ tú?
4. Tú ____________ de San Juan, ¿no?
5. ¿De dónde ____________ Francesca?
6. Felipe ____________ de Cuba.

Gramática Forming questions *Pupil's Edition, p. 30*

Question words are used to ask *who?, what?, where?, when?, why?,* and *how?* Examples of question words are:

¿Cómo estás? *(How are you?)*

¿Cómo te llamas? *(What's your name?* Literally, *How are you called?)*

¿Cuántos años tienes? *(How old are you?)*

¿De dónde eres? *(Where are you from?)*

15 You're transcribing some taped interviews for the school newspaper, but you're not able to hear the entire conversations. For each of the responses below, write what the interviewer asked or said.

1. — ¿ ____?

   — Tengo quince años.

2. — ¿ ____?

   — Estoy bastante bien, gracias.

3. — ¿ ____?

   — Soy Jannie Gooden.

4. — ____

   — Soy de Managua, Nicaragua.

5. ____

   — Me llamo Lamar Dungey.

Nombre ______________________ Clase ____________ Fecha ____________

TERCER PASO

To talk about what people like and don't like, you'll sometimes need to use words for various foods and pastimes.

VOCABULARIO Foods and pastimes *Pupil's Edition, p. 32*

16 Louis is having a tough time learning the new vocabulary words. Help him by putting each word from the word box under the correct heading.

el tenis · el jazz · la tarea · el béisbol · la pizza · el baloncesto · la música clásica · la clase de inglés · la fruta · la ensalada · el español · la música pop

LAS CLASES	LA COMIDA
____________	____________
____________	____________
____________	____________

LOS DEPORTES	LA MÚSICA
____________	____________
____________	____________
____________	____________

17 Several students are listing their favorite things from a specific category. Read each student's list and write the item that doesn't belong with the others.

1. ____________	el béisbol	el baloncesto	la pizza
2. ____________	el chocolate	el jazz	la música pop
3. ____________	la fruta	la natación	la comida china
4. ____________	el baloncesto	el tenis	la comida italiana
5. ____________	el voleibol	la ensalada	la natación
6. ____________	el tenis	el baloncesto	la tarea
7. ____________	la pizza	la fruta	la música rock
8. ____________	el español	la música clásica	la música pop

Gramática Nouns and definite articles *Pupil's Edition, p. 33*

In Spanish, nouns have a gender—either masculine or feminine. The definite articles **el** or **la** (meaning *the*) almost always indicate the gender of the noun. When learning a new noun, it's important to know which definite article accompanies it.

18 Complete this list of student likes and dislikes by writing the definite article that accompanies each noun.

1. ________ pizza
2. ________ natación
3. ________ béisbol
4. ________ español
5. ________ música pop
6. ________ tenis
7. ________ baloncesto
8. ________ chocolate
9. ________ fruta

19 Fill in the blanks in Ofelia's letter with the correct definite articles.

Alejandra,

¡Hola! ¿Qué tal? ¿Te gustan los deportes? Me gustan mucho. Me gustan (1) ________ voleibol, (2) ________ natación y (3) ________ baloncesto, pero me gusta más (4) ________ tenis. Es mi favorito. También me gusta (5) ________ música. Me gustan (6) ________ jazz y (7) ________ música pop. Me gustan (8) ________ clases, especialmente (9) ________ clase de inglés, pero no me gusta (10) ________ tarea. Y a ti, ¿qué te gusta hacer? ¡Chao!

Ofelia

20 Complete these statements by telling what items you like and dislike in each category. Be sure to include the definite articles in your answers.

1. *(sports)* Me gustan ______________________________,
   pero no me gustan ______________________________.
2. *(food)* Me gustan ______________________________,
   pero no me gustan ______________________________.
3. *(music)* Me gustan ______________________________,
   pero no me gustan ______________________________.
4. *(school)* Me gustan ______________________________,
   pero no me gustan ______________________________.

CAPÍTULO 2

Nombre ______________________ Clase ____________ Fecha ____________

¡Organízate!

PRIMER PASO

To talk about what you and others want and need, you'll need to use the words for various objects. You'll need to make nouns plural and use indefinite articles. You'll also need to understand when to use the subject pronouns **yo, tú, él,** and **ella.**

VOCABULARIO Classroom vocabulary *Pupil's Edition, p. 47*

1 Edward and his friends made lists of the supplies they need for school this year. First read their lists. Then complete the statements that follow to show who needs each item.

EDWARD
una mochila
un lápiz
una regla

KHALED
un libro
una calculadora
un bolígrafo

JENNIFER
un diccionario
papel
un cuaderno

NORA
una mochila
un libro
una goma de borrar

ETTA
una carpeta
una goma de borrar
una regla

1. ______________ needs a backpack, a pencil, and a ruler.
2. ______________ needs a dictionary, paper, and a notebook.
3. ______________ needs a backpack, a book, and an eraser.
4. ______________ needs a book, a calculator, and a pen.
5. ______________ needs a folder, an eraser, and a ruler.

2 Greg is planning to buy school supplies. Fill in the blanks with the Spanish word that best describes what he would need to . . .

1. carry his books. ______________
2. look up new words. ______________
3. organize loose papers. ______________
4. erase something. ______________
5. write notes in. ______________
6. write a draft. ______________
7. do math problems. ______________
8. measure something. ______________

CAPÍTULO 2 Primer paso

Nombre ____________________ Clase ____________ Fecha ____________

Nota Gramatical

Indefinite articles *Pupil's Edition, p. 47*

In Spanish, the indefinite articles **un** and **una** are the equivalent of *a* or *an*.

- **Un** is used with masculine nouns like **un cuaderno.**
- **Una** is used with feminine nouns like **una mochila.**

3 Determine the gender of the following nouns by writing them in the correct category.

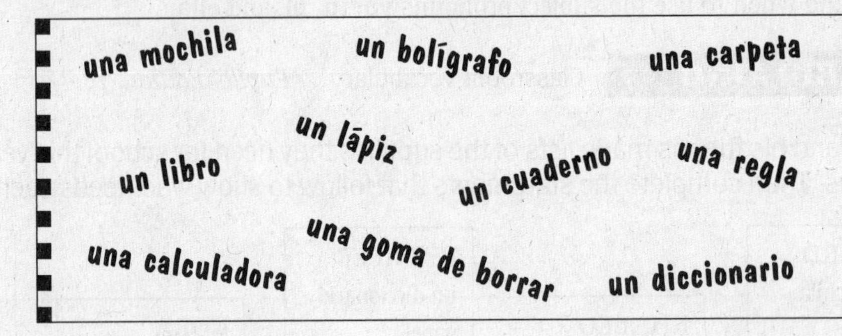

MASCULINE NOUNS	FEMININE NOUNS
____________________	____________________
____________________	____________________
____________________	____________________
____________________	____________________
____________________	____________________

4 Several students are saying what they need for classes this year. Fill in the blanks in their statements with the correct indefinite article.

1. — Yo necesito ____________________ bolígrafo.
2. — Enrique necesita ____________________ regla para su clase de matemáticas.
3. — Liliana quiere ____________________ mochila.
4. — Yo quiero ____________________ goma de borrar.
5. — Yo quiero ____________________ diccionario para mi clase de español.
6. — Tú necesitas ____________________ carpeta, ¿no?
7. — Yo necesito ____________________ libro para la clase de inglés.
8. — Ya tengo ____________________ lápiz, pero necesito otro.
9. — Yo necesito ____________________ cuaderno para la clase de francés.
10. — Carlos quiere ____________________ calculadora para su clase de álgebra.

Nombre ______________________ Clase ______________ Fecha ______________

*G*ramática   Making nouns plural   *Pupil's Edition, p. 48*

- To make a noun plural, add **-s** if it ends in a vowel: **pizza → pizzas**
- If the noun ends in a consonant, add **-es: pincel → pinceles**
- For nouns ending in -z, change -z to -c and add **-es: lápiz → lápices**

5 Clara picked the wrong list when she started packing for school. Correct her list by making the singular nouns *plural* and the plural nouns *singular.*

1. mochila ______________________
2. bolígrafo ______________________
3. libro ______________________
4. regla ______________________
5. carpeta ______________________
6. calculadoras ______________________
7. lápices ______________________
8. diccionarios ______________________
9. cuadernos ______________________
10. gomas de borrar ______________________

6 Mr. Sánchez is taking an inventory of the items in his classroom. Help him by writing the numbers with the plural forms of the nouns below.

MODELO 13 (diccionario) **trece diccionarios**

1. 8 (carpeta) ______________________
2. 4 (pizarra) ______________________
3. 10 (bolígrafo) ______________________
4. 3 (calculadora) ______________________
5. 20 (marcador) ______________________
6. 9 (lápiz) ______________________
7. 30 (libro) ______________________
8. 15 (goma de borrar) ______________________
9. 25 (regla) ______________________
10. 14 (mochila) ______________________

Nombre ______________________ Clase ____________ Fecha ____________

Gramática Indefinite articles *Pupil's Edition, p. 49*

- The plural indefinite articles **unos** and **unas** mean *some* or *a few*.
- Use **unos** with a masculine plural noun. When referring to a group that includes masculine and feminine objects or males and females, the masculine plural is used.

unos estudiantes **unos profesores**

7 Silvia has written in her planner a list of what she needs to do tomorrow, but she has left several words out. Fill in the blanks with the correct indefinite articles.

Necesito comprar:

1. ______________ *calculadora y* ______________ *regla para la clase de álgebra.*
2. ______________ *lápices y* ______________ *marcador para la clase de arte.*
3. ______________ *mochila roja.*
4. ______________ *bolígrafo para la clase de inglés.*
5. ______________ *cuadernos y* ______________ *carpetas para todas las clases.*
6. ______________ *diccionario para la clase de español.*
7. ______________ *gomas de borrar.*

8 You're filling your backpack with the items you will need for your classes tomorrow. Write three items you'll put in your bag for each of the following subjects. Be sure to use indefinite articles.

1. para la clase de español: ______________________________
2. para la clase de geometría: ______________________________
3. para la clase de inglés: ______________________________
4. para la clase de arte: ______________________________

CAPÍTULO 2 Primer paso

Nombre ______________________ Clase ____________ Fecha ____________

Nota Gramatical Subject pronouns *Pupil's Edition, p. 50*

- The subject pronoun **yo** *(I)* is used when you're talking about yourself and **tú** *(you)* is used when you're talking to a friend.

  Yo necesito tres carpetas. **Tú** necesitas dos cuadernos, ¿verdad?

- The subject pronouns **él** *(he)* or **ella** *(she)* are used when you're talking about someone else.

  Manuel y Sara son mis amigos. **Él** es del Perú. **Ella** es de Chile.

- In Spanish, subject pronouns are used mainly for clarity or emphasis, since the verb shows who the subject of the sentence is.

9 Your teacher has asked Mónica to walk around the room and introduce herself and others. Fill in the blanks with the correct subject pronoun.

1. _____ *soy Mónica Buendía.*
2. _____ *es Juan Pablo Sánchez.*
3. _____ *eres Sezai Birinçi, ¿no?*
4. _____ *es Melissa Johnson.*
5. _____ *es una amiga.*

10 Margaret is just learning how to work with subject pronouns. Which pronoun would she use when . . .?

_____ 1. describing herself

_____ 2. describing a male classmate

_____ 3. talking to a friend

_____ 4. describing a female neighbor

_____ 5. describing your male cousin

_____ 6. talking about your friend's mother

_____ 7. talking to her best friend

_____ 8. describing your uncle

_____ 9. telling someone where she's from

_____ 10. telling someone how old she is

CAPÍTULO 2 Primer paso

Nombre ______________________ Clase ____________ Fecha ____________

SEGUNDO PASO

To describe the contents of your room, you'll need to use the appropriate vocabulary. You'll also need to use the adjectives **mucho** and **cuánto.**

VOCABULARIO Bedroom vocabulary *Pupil's Edition, p. 52*

11 Lily has a summer job working in a hotel in Santo Domingo. It's her responsibility to inventory the rooms periodically to be sure all of the furniture is there. Combine the elements given to say how many of each items are in the room. You may want to use the words in the word box. Use **hay** in your sentences.

lámpara	**escritorio**	**cama**	**silla**	**reloj**	
revista	**mesa**	**ventana**	**cartel**	**radio**	**armario**

MODELO 3 / posters **Hay tres carteles.**

1. 2 / beds
____
2. 1 / closet
____
3. 3 / lamps
____
4. 4 / chairs
____
5. 1 / table
____
6. 1 / clock
____
7. 1 / desk
____

12 In the blank provided, write the item that doesn't belong with the others.

1. ______________ ventana escritorio puerta
2. ______________ escritorio mesa radio
3. ______________ zapatilla de tenis revista libro
4. ______________ reloj cartel mesa
5. ______________ radio televisor armario

CAPÍTULO 2 Segundo paso

Gramática Agreement of **mucho** and **cuánto** *Pupil's Edition, p. 54*

- In Spanish, many adjectives have endings that change depending on whether the noun is masculine or feminine (agreement in gender), singular or plural (agreement in number). These changes are shown in the following chart:

	Singular	*Plural*
Masculine	buen<u>o</u>	buen<u>os</u>
Feminine	buen<u>a</u>	buen<u>as</u>

- Various forms of **¿cuánto?** are used to ask *how much?* or *how many?* **¿Cuánto?** is an adjective, so it agrees with the noun it is describing.

  ¿Cuánto papel necesitas? **¿Cuánta** tarea tienes?
  ¿Cuántos libros hay? **¿Cuántas** carpetas quieres?

- The adjective **mucho** *(a lot, much, many)* also agrees in number and gender.

	Singular	*Plural*
Masculine	much<u>o</u>	much<u>os</u>
Feminine	much<u>a</u>	much<u>as</u>

Hay **muchos** libros, **muchas** mochilas y **mucho** papel.
Tengo **mucha** tarea para la clase de español.

13 You're taking a survey to find out what things your classmates have in their rooms. Read the following sentences or questions and fill in the blanks with the correct form of **cuánto** or **mucho.**

1. ¿______________________ carteles hay en el cuarto? (cuánto)
2. ¿______________________ revistas hay? (cuánto)
3. ¿______________________ gomas de borrar hay en el escritorio? (cuánto)
4. ¿______________________ lápices necesitas? (cuánto)
5. ¿______________________ ventanas hay en tu cuarto? (cuánto)

Now, you're announcing some of the results of your survey. Fill in the blanks with the correct form of **mucho.**

6. Tengo ______________________ bolígrafos. (mucho)
7. Necesito ______________________ cuadernos. (mucho)
8. Hay ______________________ ropa en el armario. (mucho)
9. Mónica tiene ______________________ sillas en su cuarto. (mucho)
10. Luis tiene ______________________ zapatillas de tenis. (mucho)
11. Raúl necesita ______________________ gomas de borrar. (mucho)

TERCER PASO

To talk about what you need and want to do, you'll need to use infinitives. You'll also need to use numbers from 31 to 199.

VOCABULARIO Expressions with **necesitar** and **querer** *Pupil's Edition, p. 57*

14 Silvia and Mario are talking about what they have to do or want to do this weekend. Fill in the blanks with the verbs in the word box. Some of the verbs will be used more than once.

comprar	conocer	encontrar	poner	ir

SILVIA Yo necesito (1) ______________ mis cosas en el armario. Mi cuarto está muy desorganizado. También, quiero (2) ______________ mi dinero. Necesito (3) ______________ el libro para la clase de inglés.

MARIO Bueno, yo quiero (4) ______________ al centro comercial. Si quieres, podemos (5) ______________ juntos.

SILVIA Buena idea. Pero tengo que (6) ______________ a Linda y Michael en la plaza a las cinco. ¿Quieres (7) ______________ a mis amigos?

MARIO Sí. ¡Vamos a la plaza a las cinco!

Nota Gramatical Infinitives *Pupil's Edition, p. 57*

Verbs like **comprar** *(to buy)*, **poner** *(to put)*, **conocer** *(to know, to meet)*, and **ir** *(to go)*, are called infinitives.

- In English, infinitives begin with the word *to: to run, to walk, to live.* In Spanish, infinitives always end with **-ar**, **-er**, or **-ir** **(organizar, hacer, escribir)**.

15 Read what each person does before school starts and fill in the blanks with the correct infinitive from the choices given. You may use the infinitives more than once.

ir	conocer	comprar	poner

TOTSI Yo necesito (1)______________ muchos carteles para mi cuarto.

HAN-LING Dana quiere (2)______________ a unos nuevos amigos.

KERRI Tareka necesita (3)______________ unos cuadernos.

SABINE Tú necesitas (4)______________ los libros en la mochila, ¿no?

WILL ¿Quieres (5)______________ al centro comercial hoy *(today)*?

VOCABULARIO

Numbers from 31 to 199 *Pupil's Edition, p. 58*

16 When you're in a Spanish-speaking country, you'll often hear telephone numbers spoken in pairs. Match the telephone numbers on the left with the corresponding words on the right.

_____ 1. 31-42-65
_____ 2. 79-33-98
_____ 3. 6-44-46-82
_____ 4. 86-72-60
_____ 5. 54-91-50
_____ 6. 6-39-48-99
_____ 7. 70-92-47
_____ 8. 61-80-75
_____ 9. 5-42-14-02
_____ 10. 54-91-15
_____ 11. 5-42-40-13
_____ 12. 86-72-66

a. setenta y nueve, treinta y tres, noventa y ocho
b. ochenta y seis, sesenta y dos, setenta
c. setenta, noventa y dos, cuarenta y siete
d. cincuenta y cuatro, noventa y uno, cincuenta
e. treinta y uno, cuarenta y dos, sesenta y cinco
f. sesenta y uno, ochenta, setenta y cinco
g. seis, treinta y nueve, cuarenta y ocho, noventa y nueve
h. treinta y uno, cincuenta y seis, sesenta y cinco
i. cuarenta y seis, noventa y tres, ochenta y cuatro
j. ochenta y seis, setenta y dos, sesenta
k. seis, cuarenta y cuatro, cuarenta y seis, ochenta y dos
l. ochenta y seis, setenta y dos, sesenta y seis
m. cinco, cuarenta y dos, cuarenta, trece
n. cincuenta y cuatro, noventa y uno, quince
o. cinco, cuarenta y dos, catorce, cero dos

17 You're helping your parents shop for items to refurnish your room. Write how much money you need to buy the following items.

MODELO un reloj ($32) **treinta y dos dólares**

1. un televisor ($198) ______________________ dólares
2. una radio ($50) ______________________ dólares
3. un armario ($199) ______________________ dólares
4. un teléfono ($60) ______________________ dólares
5. un reloj ($15) ______________________ dólares
6. una mesa ($75) ______________________ dólares
7. una lámpara ($46) ______________________ dólares
8. una silla ($80) ______________________ dólares
9. un escritorio ($185) ______________________ dólares
10. dos carteles ($36) ______________________ dólares
11. una cama ($199) ______________________ dólares

CAPÍTULO 3

Nombre ______________________ Clase ____________ Fecha ____________

Nuevas clases, nuevos amigos

PRIMER PASO

To talk about class schedules and to sequence events, you'll need to use the names of academic subjects. To tell time, you'll need to use numbers and some forms of the verb **ser**.

VOCABULARIO Academic subjects *Pupil's Edition, p. 75*

1 Ms. Sosa is a new advisor at school and she's helping students choose two electives for next semester. Based on each student's interests, write two classes that he or she might enjoy.

las matemáticas	el arte	la geografía	las ciencias
la educación física	la computación	el francés	las ciencias sociales

1. Mauricio enjoys sculpting, painting, and learning foreign languages.

   ______________________ y ______________________

2. Melinda likes computers and working with numbers.

   ______________________ y ______________________

3. Becky enjoys playing softball and wants to be a veterinarian.

   ______________________ y ______________________

4. Teodoro likes drawing and finding out about different countries.

   ______________________ y ______________________

5. Laura likes learning about society and would like to be an accountant.

   ______________________ y ______________________

2 Agnes has chicken pox, so her friend Julie is picking up this week's assignments for her. Julie forgot to write the subjects for each of the assignments. Help Agnes figure out which class each assignment is for.

1. pintar un autorretrato *(self-portrait)* ______________________
2. dibujar un mapa de España ______________________
3. leer el poema *"Chanson de Jacques et son chat Marcel"* ______________________
4. memorizar las tablas de multiplicar ______________________
5. estudiar el sistema de respiración ______________________

Nota Gramatical — Plural definite articles *Pupil's Edition, p. 75*

- For the word *the*, use **los** with plural masculine nouns.
  los libros, los cuadernos, los amigos
- Use **las** with plural feminine nouns.
  las camas, las lámparas, las amigas

3 Mr. Gómez is taking an inventory of supplies to distribute to his students for the new school year. Write the correct definite article for each item he has for his students.

1. ________ cuadernos	6. ________ lápices
2. ________ gomas de borrar	7. ________ reglas
3. ________ diccionario	8. ________ libros
4. ________ carpetas	9. ________ calculadoras
5. ________ revistas	10. ________ bolígrafos

4 Jeff has just taken a job as a waiter at Ana's Pizzeria. Fill in the blanks with the correct definite articles to complete his passage about the items he encounters at his new job.

A ver... en (1) ________ pizzería hay muchas cosas. (2) ________ sillas y (3) ________ mesas son para todos (4) ________ clientes que están en el restaurante. (5) ________ comida italiana, (6) ________ ensaladas y (7) ________ pizzas son muy populares. También (8) ________ chocolate y (9) ________ frutas son muy deliciosos.

5 Read the following dialogues and fill in the blanks with the correct definite articles.

MAMÁ ¿Qué quieres para (1) ________ clases este semestre?

JUANITO Bueno, Mamá, quiero (2) ________ zapatillas de tenis que están de moda *(in style)*.

* * *

ABUELA ¿Tienes (3) ________ cosas que te compré *(I bought for you)* en tu mochila?

SUNITA Sí. Tengo (4) ________ cuadernos, (5) ________ bolígrafos, (6) ________ diccionario y (7) ________ calculadora.

* * *

PROFESOR ¿Dónde están (8) ________ libros?

KENYATTA Tengo (9) ________ libros y (10) ________ revistas en mi escritorio, Profesor Sánchez.

*G*ramática Telling time *Pupil's Edition, p. 78*

- To tell the time, use **Son las...** plus the hour.

  Son las dos. **Son las** cuatro. **Son las** diez.

- After the hour, add the minutes with the word **y** *(and)*.

  Son las seis **y diez.** Son las siete **y media.** Son las once **y cuarto.**

- After the half hour, subtract the minutes to the next hour with the word **menos** *(minus)*.

  Son las cinco **menos veinte.**

  Son las tres **menos cuarto.**

- For times including one o'clock, use **Es la...**

  Es la una. **Es la** una y veinte.

6 Valerie is spending Saturday afternoon working in her grandmother's clock store. Her task is to set the correct time on a shipment of new clocks. In Spanish, help Valerie catalog the new shipment by matching each clock to the correct time.

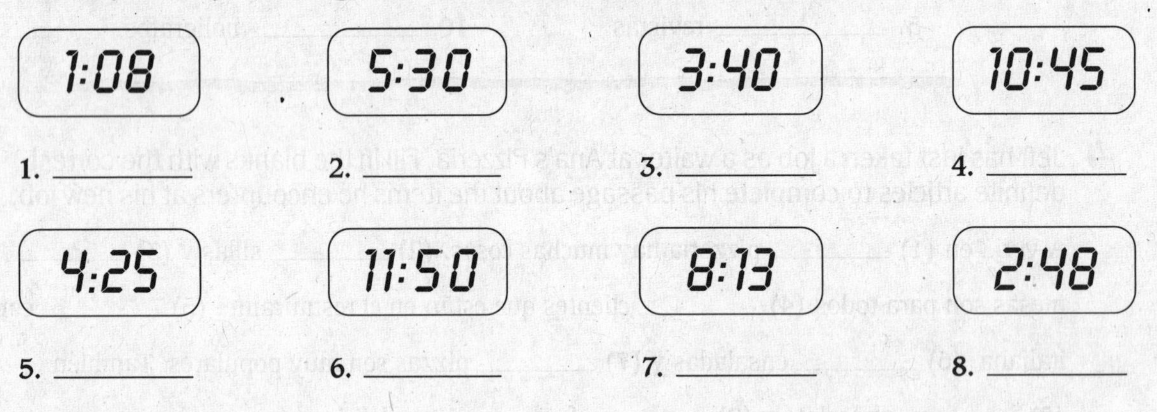

a. Son las doce menos diez.
b. Son las cuatro menos veinte.
c. Son las tres menos doce.
d. Son las ocho y trece.
e. Son las once menos cuarto.
f. Es la una y ocho.
g. Son las cuatro y veinticinco.
h. Son las cinco y media.
i. Es la una y media.

7 Fernando, a radio disk jockey for a Spanish radio station in Baltimore, frequently announces the time during his shift. Write the following times he says one afternoon.

1. 12:35 ______________________________
2. 2:04 ______________________________
3. 2:50 ______________________________
4. 3:20 ______________________________
5. 4:00 ______________________________
6. 5:30 ______________________________

Nombre ______________________ Clase ____________ Fecha ____________

SEGUNDO PASO

To tell at what time something happens, you'll need to respond to the question **¿A qué hora... ?**

VOCABULARIO Time expressions *Pupil's Edition, p. 80*

8 Herman programmed the computers at the airport with arrival times from particular cities. For each of the times listed below, write what the computer will display.

MODELO *Nashville* – 3:46 A.M. **A las cuatro menos catorce de la mañana.**

1. *St. Louis* – 7:40 A.M. ______________________
2. *Chicago* – 7:30 A.M. ______________________
3. *Des Moines* – 6:15 A.M. ______________________
4. *Gary* – 8:50 P.M. ______________________
5. *Detroit* – 11:25 P.M. ______________________
6. *Toledo* – 4:55 A.M. ______________________
7. *Madison* – 3:13 P.M. ______________________
8. *Dubuque* – 12:30 P.M. ______________________

9 Abby has just received her schedule for the new semester. Use the schedule to help her figure out what class she has today at each time listed below.

8:30 – 9:15	la computación
9:20 – 10:05	el arte
10:10 – 10:55	las matemáticas
11:00 – 11:45	las ciencias
11:50 – 12:30	el descanso
12:35 – 1:20	la educación física
1:25 – 2:10	la geografía
2:15 – 3:00	las ciencias sociales

MODELO Abby tiene la clase de arte **a las diez menos cinco.**

1. Abby tiene la clase de educación física ______________________.
2. Abby tiene la clase de ciencias ______________________.
3. Abby tiene la clase de ciencias sociales ______________________.
4. Abby tiene la clase de geografía ______________________.
5. Abby tiene la clase de matemáticas ______________________.
6. Abby tiene la clase de arte ______________________.

Nota Gramatical — Possession using **de** *Pupil's Edition, p. 81*

To show possession in Spanish, use **de.** This is the equivalent of *-'s* (apostrophe *s*) in English.

los cuadernos de Eva *Eva's notebooks*
la mochila de Pablo *Paul's backpack*
el libro de Anita y Eduardo *Anita and Edward's book*
los lápices de Carlos y Felipe *Carlos and Felipe's pencils*

10 Chris and Bob have just moved into their new home. Write the following items they have unpacked.

MODELO lamp / Chris **la lámpara de Chris**

1. posters / Bob ______
2. tennis shoes / Chris ______
3. clothing / Bob ______
4. radio / Chris ______
5. table / Bob ______
6. magazines / Chris ______
7. TV set / Bob ______
8. clock / Chris ______
9. chair / Bob ______

11 It's a busy Monday morning for Mr. Contreras! The dining room table is covered with his children's school supplies and he's trying to figure out what items belong to which child. Follow the model to help him out.

MODELO Silvia's folders **Las carpetas son de Silvia.**

1. Eduardo and Lupe's books ______
2. Silvia's pens ______
3. Lupe and Eduardo's pencils ______
4. Lupe's erasers ______
5. Eduardo's ruler ______
6. Silvia's backpack ______
7. Lupe's dictionary ______
8. Silvia and Eduardo's papers ______
9. Silvia's notebooks ______

TERCER PASO

To describe people and things, you'll need to use the verb **ser** and adjectives. To talk about things you like and explain why, you'll need to use the verb **gustar**.

Nota Gramatical The verb **ser** *Pupil's Edition, p. 84*

The verb **ser** *(to be)* is an irregular verb. It conjugates as follows:

yo **soy**	nosotros **somos**
tú **eres**	vosotros sois
él, ella, usted **es**	ellos, ellas, ustedes **son**

12 Bobby Dan Hatfield has written a note to Marco, his pen pal in Bolivia, about himself and his friends. Complete his note with the correct forms of the verb **ser**.

¡Hola Marco!

Me llamo Bobby Dan y (1) ______ de Portland, Oregon. Yo (2) ______ inteligente y bajo. También (3) ______ guapo y un poco cómico. ¿Y mis amigos? Bueno, ellos (4) ______ amigos muy buenos. Una amiga (5) ______ Cindy. Ella (6) ______ muy bonita. Otro amigo, Louis, (7) ______ muy divertido. Cindy y Louis (8) ______ muy simpáticos. Nosotros (9) ______ muy buenos amigos. Y, ¿cómo (10) ______ tú?

Tu amigo, Bobby Dan

13 Answer the following questions about yourself and your friends in complete sentences.

1. ¿De dónde eres? ______
2. ¿De dónde es tu profesor(a) de español? ______
3. ¿Cómo eres? ______
4. ¿Cómo es tu mejor(a) amigo(a)? ______
5. ¿De dónde son tus padres? ______

CAPÍTULO 3 Tercer paso

Nombre ______________________ Clase __________ Fecha __________

VOCABULARIO Adjectives *Pupil's Edition, p. 84*

14 Rosa is describing some famous people and characters to her best friend Dena, but Dena can't figure out who is who! Help her out by matching the description on the left with the correct person or character on the right.

1. ________ Son morenos y muy guapos.
2. ________ Es muy alto y feo.
3. ________ Es morena, baja y bonita.
4. ________ Son rubias y bonitas.
5. ________ Son muy inteligentes.
6. ________ Es guapo y rubio.

a. Brad Pitt
b. Claudia Schiffer y Heather Locklear
c. Frankenstein
d. Gloria Estefan
e. Antonio Banderas y Andy García
f. Albert Einstein y Marie Curie

15 Fernando is describing some of his friends to his grandfather. Help him out by creating sentences using the cues provided.

MODELO Clara (cómico) **Clara es cómica.**

1. Juan y Pepe (alto) ________________________
2. Eva (bajo y bonito) ________________________
3. Silvia y Laura (inteligente) ________________________
4. Pablo y Teodoro (guapo y rubio) ________________________
5. Diana y Carlos (divertido y simpático) ________________________

16 Now it's your turn! Describe each of the following people with three adjectives from the **Vocabulario** box on page 84 of your textbook.

MODELO Mi profesora favorita **es la señora Dakhlia. Ella es inteligente, cómica y muy simpática.**

1. Mi profesor favorito ________________________.
2. Mi actriz favorita ________________________.
3. Mi actor favorito ________________________.
4. Mi clase favorita ________________________.

Nombre ______________________ Clase __________ Fecha __________

Gramática Adjective agreement *Pupil's Edition, p. 85*

- Adjectives change to match the number and gender of the nouns they modify.

	Masculine	*Feminine*
Singular	un amigo cómico	una amiga cómica
Plural	unos amigos cómicos	unas amigas cómicas

- When describing a group of females and males, use a masculine plural adjective.

  Eva y Juan son **antipáticos.**

- Adjectives ending in **-e** or a consonant don't match in gender, but they match in number.

  El amigo es **inteligente.** → Los amigos son **inteligentes.**
  La clase es **interesante.** → Las clases son **interesantes.**

17 Dena has now made a list of famous people with Rosa's help. Can you create sentences using the adjectives supplied for the people on her list?

1. Winona Ryder / ser / bajo y simpático
____
2. Bill Cosby / ser / inteligente y cómico
____
3. Alicia Silverstone / ser / rubio y cómico
____
4. Danny Devito / ser / divertido y bajo
____
5. Michelle Pfeiffer y Rachel Hunter / ser / rubio y bonito
____
6. Daniel Day-Lewis / ser / alto y delgado
____
7. Tom Hanks y Robin Williams / ser / bajo y guapo
____
8. Shaquille O'Neal y Michael Jordan / ser / alto y simpático
____
9. Queen Latifah y Billy Crystal / ser / inteligente y divertido
____
10. Tom Cruise y Demi Moore / ser / inteligente y guapo
____

VOCABULARIO Pastime words *Pupil's Edition, p. 87*

18 Several friends are talking about things they like. Fill in the blanks with the best word from the word box.

fiestas	partido	videojuegos	deportes
bailes	novela	concierto	examen

MUSTAFA ¿Te gusta bailar?

ANGÉLICA Sí, mis (1) ______________ favoritos son la salsa y el merengue.

* * *

LUIS ¿Cuáles son tus (2) ______________ favoritos?

ESTEBAN Me gusta el tenis, el voleibol y el béisbol.

* * *

ANTONIA ¿Te gusta leer?

ARTURO Sí, mi (3) ______________ favorita es *Cien años de soledad.*

* * *

STEPHANIE ¿Te gusta la música rock?

JULIO Sí, me gusta mucho.

STEPHANIE ¿Quieres ir al (4) ______________ de música conmigo?

* * *

GABRIEL Me gustan mucho las (5) ______________.

FÁTIMA ¿Por qué?

GABRIEL Porque allí puedes bailar, escuchar música y celebrar con tus amigos.

19 Write the correct form of the verb **gustar** in the blanks. Remember that **gustar** takes a pronoun (**me, le,** or **te**).

MODELO A mí me gusta la comida china.

1. A Susana ______________ su perro.
2. A mí ______________ la comida italiana de la cafetería.
3. A Sung ______________ el baile folklórico.
4. ¿A ti ______________ los partidos de fútbol americano?
5. A mi amigo ______________ los conciertos de la música clásica.
6. Al profesor Cisneros ______________ los libros de literatura española.
7. ¿A ti ______________ la clase de educación física con la profesora Jiménez?
8. A mí ______________ los centros comerciales porque ______________ comprar ropa.

CAPÍTULO 4

Nombre ______________________ Clase ____________ Fecha ____________

¿Qué haces esta tarde?

PRIMER PASO

To talk about what you like to do during your free time, you'll need to use the present tense. You'll also need to use the words **con** *(with)* and **que** *(that, which,* or *who)* to say with whom you do these activities.

VOCABULARIO Activities around the house *Pupil's Edition, p. 101*

1 Jamila and several friends are discussing what they like to do on weekends. Choose the infinitive from the word box that best completes each sentence.

lavar	escuchar	cuidar	descansar	nadar
mirar		dibujar	pintar	sacar

JAMILA A mí me gusta (1) ______________ la televisión.

PERCY Me gusta (2) ______________ en el parque.

JULIO A mí me gusta el parque también. Especialmente me gusta (3) ______________ en la piscina.

LEN A mí me gusta (4) ______________ música.

ELI Berta, te gusta el arte, ¿verdad? ¿Te gusta (5) ______________?

BERTA Sí, a mí me gusta dibujar y (6) ______________.

RAÚL Me gusta (7) ______________ el carro de mis padres.

2 Now, Jamila's friends are talking about what they need to do this weekend. Fill in each blank with an appropriate verb from the box in Activity 1.

ELI Jamila, necesitas (1) ______________ a tu hermano también, ¿no?

LEN Yo necesito (2) ______________ la basura.

JULIO Quiero (3) ______________ la ropa.

PERCY Necesito (4) ______________ el carro.

JAMILA Yo quiero (5) ______________ para mi clase de arte.

BERTA Necesito (6) ______________ un programa de televisión para la clase de historia.

RAÚL Necesito (7) ______________ al gato *(cat)*.

Gramática Present tense of regular -ar verbs *Pupil's Edition, p. 102*

- In Spanish and English, you have to change verbs according to their subjects. This is called *conjugating* the verb.
- To conjugate a regular -**ar** verb, such as **nadar**, drop the -**ar** from the infinitive and add one of the following endings to the stem:

nadar → nad-

(yo) -**o** → nad<u>o</u> *I swim*	(nosotros) -**amos** → nad**amos** *we swim*
(tú) -**as** → nad**as** *you swim*	(vosotros) -áis → nadáis *you* (pl., Spain) *swim*
(él, ella, usted) -**a** → nad<u>a</u> *he/ she/ you swim(s)*	(ellos, ellas, ustedes) -**an** → nad**an** *you* (pl.) *swim, they swim*

3 Alma is working as a counselor at summer camp. She has written a list of what some campers are doing there. Fill in the blanks with the correct forms of the verbs given in parentheses.

... Ulani (1) ______________________ (tocar) la guitarra. Cristina y Zahara (2) ______________________ (practicar) deportes. Renaldo (3) ______________________ (dibujar). Tyrone (4) ______________________ (escuchar) música. Abasi y Theo (5) ______________________ (descansar). Nuru (6) ______________________ (lavar) la ropa. René (7) ______________________ (hablar) por teléfono ...

4 Alma's mother has just received the above letter and is going to write a response. Help her write a letter to Alma by forming sentences using the elements below.

MODELO Harry / hablar con sus amigos **Harry habla con sus amigos.**

1. Miguel / estudiar / todos los días

____

2. Rosita y Daphne / cantar en el coro *(choir)*

____

3. Yo / no / bailar mucho

____

4. Nosotros / mirar / la televisión / bastante

____

5 In the letter that Alma's parents are writing, they also want to ask her what activities she and her new friends are doing. Use the following fragments to write questions.

MODELO Luis / hablar mucho por teléfono **¿Habla Luis mucho por teléfono?**

1. Tus amigas / escuchar música

   ¿______________________________?
2. Tú / nadar en la piscina

   ¿______________________________?
3. Tú y tus amigos / lavar el carro

   ¿______________________________?
4. Tú / sacar la basura / todos los días

   ¿______________________________?

6 Write four sentences about yourself and your friends and family.

1. (yo) hablar por teléfono ______________________________
2. (mis amigos) nadar ______________________________
3. (mi padre) sacar la basura ______________________________
4. (mi famila y yo) mirar la televisión ______________________________

____

VOCABULARIO

Pastime activities *Pupil's Edition, p. 103*

7 Tanya has made a list of the things she plans to do today. Complete the statements and then circle the activities that she planned to do on the following puzzle.

1. ______________ *con el perro*
2. ______________ *el rato con amigos*
3. ______________ *en bicicleta*
4. ______________ *la cena*
5. ______________ *un refresco*
6. ______________ *en un restaurante*

P	A	T	C	A	M	B	Y	Y	B	K
H	I	D	O	T	X	A	H	E	Z	H
D	A	N	A	M	D	V	N	M	O	A
U	F	I	D	A	A	D	Z	E	Q	L
T	R	P	A	S	A	R	S	N	A	E
H	A	R	B	K	P	A	U	I	L	D
B	F	E	H	T	E	R	R	C	I	J
T	H	P	L	M	O	N	T	A	R	E
R	C	A	I	K	E	R	R	M	O	N
A	H	R	D	N	M	K	L	I	P	N
B	E	A	E	B	R	X	Z	N	O	I
A	D	R	N	A	S	F	D	A	I	H
J	L	T	N	A	R	O	N	R	L	I
A	I	E	S	W	E	R	T	Y	U	C
R	C	W	E	M	E	H	C	I	H	H

Nota Gramatical — The preposition **con** — *Pupil's Edition, p. 104*

- Use **con** *(with)* + the pronouns you've already learned for *him, her, them, us,* and *you* (pl.):

  Ana y Eva estudian con **nosotros.** Luis estudia con **ustedes.** Marta estudia con Pepe, y Tomás estudia con **ellos** también.

- The following expressions mean *with me* and *with you*:

  Yo practico deportes **contigo** *(with you)* y tú escuchas música **conmigo** *(with me)*. ¿De acuerdo?

8 Nora works in a dance studio. Help her direct her dancers by filling in the blanks with the correct expressions with **con**.

MODELO Rodney baila con ella. (Annette).

1. Latoya baila ______________________ (Earl y yo).
2. Dorothy baila ______________________ (Charles)
3. Nodin baila ______________________ (tú).
4. Tai Kwong baila ______________________ (Elizabeth).
5. Kareem baila ______________________ (Latisha y Ana).
6. Dwight baila ______________________ (yo).

Nota Gramatical — The word **que** — *Pupil's Edition, p. 105*

The word **que**, used to refer to people or things, means *that, which,* or *who.*

Tengo una amiga **que** habla español. *I have a friend who speaks Spanish.*

La comida **que** me gusta comer es pizza. *The food that I like to eat is pizza.*

9 Write four sentences using the fragments below.

COLUMN A	COLUMN B	COLUMN C
el muchacho	tocar el piano	Luisa
la muchacha	nadar en la piscina	Nicolás
la profesora	dibujar	Sr. González
el profesor	estudiar	Sra. Ramos
	montar en bicicleta	

1. ______________________
2. ______________________
3. ______________________
4. ______________________

Nombre ______________________ Clase ____________ Fecha ____________

SEGUNDO PASO

To talk about where people or things are, you'll need to use the verb **estar**, places in town, and prepositions of location. You'll also need to use the subject pronouns for clarity or emphasis.

Nota Gramatical

The present tense of **estar** *Pupil's Edition, p. 106*

The verb **estar** is used to talk about where things or people are located.

(Yo) **estoy** en la farmacia.	(Nosotros, nosotras) **estamos** en el cuarto.
(Tú) **estás** en el parque.	(Vosotros, vosotras) **estáis** en la clase.
(Él) **está** en la piscina.	(Ellos or Ellas) **están** en la pizzería.
(Ella) **está** en la piscina.	(Ustedes) **están** en la pizzería.
(Usted) **está** en la piscina.	

10 Taci's friend Beverly has been living in another state for the last year. Beverly has returned for the weekend and has many questions about where people and things are. Help Taci answer Beverly's questions by filling in the blanks with the correct forms of **estar.**

BEVERLY ¿Dónde **(1)** ______________________ Joan?

TACI Ella **(2)** ______________________ en Cincinnati con su abuela.

BEVERLY ¿Y Lonnie?

TACI Él **(3)** ______________________ en la biblioteca.

BEVERLY ¿Y Roland y Tomás?

TACI **(4)** ______________________ en el trabajo.

BEVERLY ¿Y Paquito?

TACI **(5)** ______________________ en su casa.

BEVERLY ¿Y Freddy y Cindy?

TACI **(6)** ______________________ en el centro.

BEVERLY ¿Y dónde **(7)** ______________________ tú y tu familia?

TACI **(8)** ______________________ en una casa en la calle Bolívar.

11 Write a sentence telling where each of the following people is now:

1. yo ____
2. mi mejor amigo(a) ____
____
3. El Presidente de los Estados Unidos ____
____
4. Mis padres ____

VOCABULARIO

Places and prepositions of location *Pupil's Edition, p. 107*

12 Help Lois solve the following riddles. Fill in the first blank with the correct form of the verb in parentheses and the second blank with the place where this would be likely to occur.

el gimnasio	el supermercado	el correo	la piscina
la biblioteca	la tienda	el parque	el cine

MODELO Khadija __________ (descansar) en __________.
Khadija **descansa** en **el parque**.

1. Rodolfo y Berta __________ (comprar) la comida en __________.
2. Sally __________ (nadar) en __________.
3. Tú __________ (comprar) ropa en __________.
4. Nosotros __________ (estudiar) para los exámenes en __________.
5. Me gusta __________ (ver) películas en __________.
6. Ustedes __________ (practicar) deportes en __________.
7. Yo __________ (necesitar) comprar estampillas en __________.

13 Aiyana has just moved to San Juan, Puerto Rico. Use the items in the word box to help her find her way around by telling where things are located according to the diagram below.

1. El Cine Nasuma está __________ del supermercado.
2. El supermercado está __________ del gimnasio.
3. La piscina está __________ del gimnasio.
4. La Tienda Saldaña está __________ del restaurante.
5. El gimnasio está __________ de la piscina.

Gramática Subject pronouns *Pupil's Edition, p. 109*

- The subject pronouns in Spanish are:

yo *(I)*	**nosotros / nosotras** *(we)*
tú *(you)*	**vosotros / vosotras** *(you)* (pl., Spain)
él *(he* or *it)*	**ellos** *(they)*
ella *(she* or *it)*	**ellas** *(they)*
usted *(you)* (formal)	**ustedes** *(you)* (pl.)

- **Usted** (abbreviated **Ud.**) and **tú** both mean *you.* Use **tú** (the familiar *you*) when talking to a friend, a family member, or someone your own age or younger. Use **usted** (the formal *you*) when talking to an adult who isn't a family member. In the Americas, *you* (pl.) is always **ustedes**.
- **Ellos** and **ellas** both mean *they*. Use **ellas** when you're talking about a group of females. Use **ellos** if you're talking about a group of males or a group of males and females together.

14 The following statements tell what you and your classmates do. Rewrite the statements by replacing the underlined portion with the correct subject pronoun.

MODELO Vicky quiere nadar. → **Ella** quiere nadar.

1. Robert y Jeremy preparan la cena. ______
2. Tabitha y Janie miran la televisión. ______
3. Todd y Felicia nadan en la piscina. ______
4. Nancy camina con el perro. ______
5. Jerome toma un helado. ______
6. Mario y yo necesitamos trabajar. ______

15 Would you use **tú** or **usted** to address these people?

1. tu amigo Samuel ______
2. tu profesor de inglés ______
3. la madre de tu amiga ______
4. tu profesora de francés ______
5. tu amiga Mavis ______
6. tu papá ______

16 How would you . . . ?

1. ask the principal of your school how she or he is

   ¿______?
2. tell your younger sister that she talks a lot on the telephone

   ______.
3. ask your friend Juan if he watches television

   ¿______?
4. ask your Spanish teacher if he or she plays the piano

   ¿______?

TERCER PASO

To talk about where you and others go during free time, you'll need to use the verb **ir** and the days of the week with definite articles.

Nota Gramatical The verb ir *Pupil's Edition, p. 111*

The verb **ir** *(to go)* is conjugated as follows:

yo **voy**	nosotros **vamos**
tú **vas**	vosotros **vais**
él, ella, usted **va**	ellos, ellas, ustedes **van**

17 Several of Adolfo's friends are going on vacation. Fill in the blanks with the correct form of **ir** to say where he and his friends are going.

1. Alicia y yo ____________ a Inglaterra.
2. Y luego yo ____________ a España.
3. Pablo ____________ a Japón.
4. Norma, tú ____________ a Perú, ¿no?
5. Arlon y Félix ____________ a Bolivia.
6. Nannette y Silvia ____________ a Rusia.
7. Señora, usted ____________ a Australia, ¿no?
8. Ustedes ____________ a Argentina, ¿verdad?

18 All of your friends are going somewhere this weekend. Combine words and phrases from all three columns to say where they are going.

COLUMN A		COLUMN B
Priscilla		al centro
Juan Carlos		a la biblioteca
Yo		al cine
Tú	+ IR +	a la ciudad
Usted		al restaurante
Ustedes		a la piscina
Eva y yo		al parque
Bruce y Franklin		al gimnasio

MODELO **Priscilla va al restaurante.**

1. ______________________________
2. ______________________________
3. ______________________________
4. ______________________________
5. ______________________________
6. ______________________________
7. ______________________________

VOCABULARIO

Days of the week *Pupil's Edition, p. 112*

19 Cindy has been very busy lately. Look at her schedule and answer the questions about when she is going to do different activities.

lunes	martes	miércoles	jueves	viernes	sábado	domingo
ir a un concierto con Manuel	nadar en la piscina de Mónica	ir al cine con Corey y Khira	estudiar en la biblioteca	ir al restaurante con mis padres	montar en bicicleta en el parque	jugar al tenis con Felipe

1. ¿Cuándo *(When)* va a escuchar música? ______________________
2. ¿Cuándo va a hacer ejercicio? ______________________ ,
   y ______________________
3. ¿Cuándo va a ver una película? ______________________
4. ¿Cuándo va a comer con sus padres? ______________________
5. ¿Cuándo va a estudiar? ______________________

20 On the following calendar, write the names of the weekdays and what you're planning to do for each day. Use the following guidelines: Mondays are exercise days, Tuesdays are outdoor days, Wednesdays are study days, Thursdays are work days and Fridays are days to be with friends. The first entry has been done for you.

montar en bicicleta · **descansar en el parque** · **bailar con mis amigos** · **nadar** · **trabajar** · **ir a la biblioteca** · **mirar la televisión** · **cantar** · **pasar el rato con amigo**

lunes				
nadar con mis amigos				

Nota Gramatical

Expressions with days of the week *Pupil's Edition, p. 112*

- To say that you do something on a particular day, use **el** + the day of the week.

  El viernes voy al cine con Mathilde.
  On Friday, I'm going to the movies with Mathilde.
- To say that you do something regularly on a certain day, use **los** + the day.

  Los viernes ceno con mis padres.
  On Fridays, I have dinner with my parents.
- You do not use **el** or **los** before the day when you say what day of the week it is.

  Hoy es lunes. *Today is Monday.*
- The days of the week are not capitalized in Spanish text.

21 For these sentences, decide whether the event is taking place **(O)** once on a particular day, **(R)** regularly on a certain day, or **(D)** if the statement is telling what day it is today.

1. _____ Nado en la piscina los lunes.
2. _____ Miro la televisión los martes.
3. _____ El jueves voy al café con David.
4. _____ Cristóbal va a trabajar el domingo.
5. _____ Voy al parque el sábado.
6. _____ Hoy es miércoles.

22 Sofie is trying to make plans with her friend Alex, who is always busy. Fill in the blanks with **el** or **los** to complete each sentence. In one blank, you won't need an article. Mark an **X** in that blank.

SOFIE (1) ______________ viernes, voy a comer con mis padres. Vamos a celebrar mi cumpleaños *(birthday)*. ¿Quieres ir con nosotros?

ALEX Gracias, pero no puedo. (2) ______________ viernes siempre estudio música.

SOFIE Vale. Oye, ¿qué haces (3) ______________ sábado?

ALEX (4) ______________ sábados voy al cine con mi primo Carlos.

SOFIE ¿Y esta noche?

ALEX Hoy es (5) ______________ martes; puedo hacer algo contigo.

SOFIE ¡Excelente! Vamos al parque.

23 Write one or two things you regularly do on the following days of the week.

1. (los lunes) ______________________________
2. (los martes) ______________________________
3. (los viernes) ______________________________
4. (los sábados) ______________________________
5. (los domingos) ______________________________

Nombre ____________ Clase ____________ Fecha ____________

El ritmo de la vida

PRIMER PASO

To discuss how often you do things, you might use the word *never.* Other negative words like *never* are *nothing* and *no one.*

Gramática Negation *Pupil's Edition, p. 129*

To make a negative sentence, either put the negative word before the verb *or* put **no** before the verb and the negative word after the verb.

nunca	*(never, not ever)*	**Nunca** hablo por teléfono. **No** hablo por teléfono **nunca**.
nada	*(nothing)*	**No** tengo **nada** en la mochila.
nadie	*(nobody)*	**Nadie** mira la televisión. **No** mira la televisión **nadie**.

1 Pepe, a reporter for the school newspaper, is interviewing Rita Ramírez, a star athlete at his school. Read this portion of their interview, underline all of the expressions that tell how often she does the activities she mentions, and then select the option that best completes each sentence according to their conversation.

PEPE Rita, ¿con qué frecuencia montas en bicicleta?

RITA ¡Monto en bicicleta todos los días!

PEPE ¿Siempre nadas en la piscina también?

RITA No, no siempre, pero nado en la piscina muchas veces durante la semana. Nado sólo cuando tengo tiempo.

PEPE Y Rita, ¿te gusta hablar por teléfono?

RITA ¡No me gusta hablar por teléfono para nada! Nunca hablo por teléfono.

1. Rita siempre ____________.
2. Rita nunca ____________.
3. Rita ____________ sólo cuando tiene tiempo.

a. monta en bicicleta
b. nada
c. habla por teléfono
d. trabaja
e. dibuja

CAPÍTULO 5 Primer paso

Nombre ______________________ Clase ____________ Fecha ____________

2 Some of Mr. Edwards' students are very conscientious, but others are not! Complete his descriptions of the students by writing a negative sentence that contrasts with the affirmative ones. The first one has been done for you.

1. Mónica siempre cuida a su hermano los fines de semana. (Silvia / nunca)

   Pero Silvia nunca cuida a su hermano.
2. Alguien lee revistas en la biblioteca. (nadie / hacer la tarea)

   ____
3. Pablo y Sofía siempre caminan con el perro en el parque. (sus hermanos / nunca / ir al parque)

   ____
4. Todos miran la televisión. (nadie / mirar el Canal 13)

   ____
5. Luis y Fernando siempre van al parque para jugar al tenis. (Ernesto / nunca)

   ____

3 Write sentences telling how often or when you do the following activities.

MODELO ¿Tocas la guitarra? **Nunca toco la guitarra.**

1. ¿Miras la televisión? ______________________________
2. ¿Organizas tu cuarto? ______________________________
3. ¿Montas en bicicleta? ______________________________
4. ¿Trabajas con la computadora? ______________________________
5. ¿Practicas deportes? ______________________________
6. ¿Tocas la guitarra? ______________________________

Nota Gramatical ¿quién? and ¿quiénes? *Pupil's Edition, p. 130*

Use **¿quién?** to ask about one person: **¿Quién** es la chica bonita y baja?

Use **¿quiénes?** to ask about more than one person: **¿Quiénes** son ellos?

4 Ms. Carter is a new high school Spanish teacher at school. Complete her questions about everyone by filling in the blanks with **quién** or **quiénes**.

1. ¿ ____________ es el chico moreno?
2. ¿ ____________ son las chicas en la oficina?
3. ¿ ____________ es la chica alta y morena?
4. ¿ ____________ es la profesora alta y rubia?
5. ¿ ____________ son los chicos rubios?
6. ¿ ____________ es el profesor bajo y guapo?

Nombre ______________ Clase ______________ Fecha ______________

SEGUNDO PASO

To talk about what you and your friends like to do together, you'll need to use **gustar.** To talk about what you do during a typical week, you'll need to use phrases that express how often something happens.

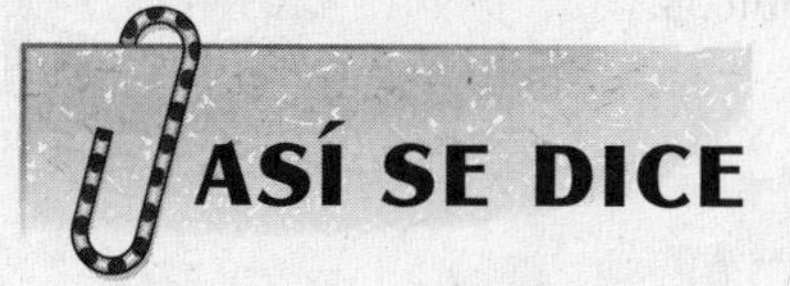

Talking about what you and your friends like to do together *Pupil's Edition, p. 132*

5 A busload of excited campers is headed for Camp Webegone for the summer. Many campers are chatting about activities they like to do. Complete their conversations with the words from the word box.

me	le	nos	te	le	les

FELICIA ¡Hola! Me llamo Felicia y éste es mi amigo Roberto. A nosotros (1) __________ gusta bucear. ¿A ustedes (2) __________ gusta bucear?

JUANITO Mucho gusto. Soy Juanito y ésta es mi amiga Raquel. A nosotros (3) __________ gusta bucear y esquiar. ¿A ustedes (4) __________ gusta esquiar?

FELICIA Bueno, a mí (5) __________ gusta mucho, pero a Roberto no (6) __________ gusta para nada.

ROBERTO Sí, sí. A mí (7) __________ gusta pescar. Raquel, ¿a ti (8) __________ gusta pescar?

RAQUEL Claro que sí, hombre. También a Juanito y a mí (9) __________ gusta mucho correr por la playa. ¿A ustedes (10) __________ gusta correr también?

FELICIA Sí. A nosotros (11) __________ gusta mucho. Oye, vamos a correr esta noche, ¿eh?

VOCABULARIO

Activities *Pupil's Edition, p. 133*

6 Claudia is writing a rough draft of a composition for Spanish class about her family, but she's gotten her notes all mixed up. Help her out by choosing the best completion for each of her sentences and writing it in the blank.

1. A mi padre le gusta comer __________.
2. A mi abuela le gusta escribir __________.
3. A mí me gusta asistir a __________.
4. A mi hermana Sofía le gusta beber __________.
5. A mis hermanos y a mí nos gusta leer __________.

a. una clase de ejercicios aeróbicos
b. cartas
c. un sándwich
d. jugo
e. las tiras cómicas

CAPÍTULO 5 Segundo paso

Nota Gramatical Clarifying with **les gusta(n)** *Pupil's Edition, p. 133*

Since the pronoun **les** can mean *to them* or *to you (plural)*, add the phrases **a ustedes, a ellos,** or **a ellas** for clarification.

A ustedes les gusta la clase de español.

A ellos les gusta asistir a una clase de ejercicios aeróbicos.

A ellas les gustan las tiras cómicas.

7 Linda's grandparents are asking about what activities Linda and her friends enjoy. Supply Linda's responses for each of the following.

MODELO ¿Lu y Juan? (estudiar/biblioteca) **A ellos les gusta estudiar en la biblioteca.**

1. ¿Miguel y Pablo? (jugar al tenis/parque)
____

2. ¿Paula y Teresa? (comer/restaurante)
____

3. ¿Nosotros? (asisitir/clase de ejercicios aeróbicos)
____

4. ¿LaQuishi y Silviana? (hacer ejercicio/gimnasio)
____

Gramática The present tense of **-er** and **-ir** verbs *Pupil's Edition, p. 134*

- **LEER** *(to read)*
  leo, le**es**, le**e**, le**emos**, le**éis**, le**en**
- **ESCRIBIR** *(to write)*
  escrib**o**, escrib**es**, escrib**e**, escrib**imos**, escrib**ís**, escrib**en**

8 Isabel and Mario are talking about what they and their families do on Saturdays. Complete their conversation by filling in the blanks with the correct form of the verbs in parentheses.

ISABEL Mi hermana Susana siempre (1) ______________ (escribir) cartas a sus amigos. Mis padres y yo (2) ______________ (comer) en un restaurante cubano. Mis hermanos Hernán y Felipe estudian en la biblioteca y yo (3) ______________ (leer) el periódico. ¿(4) ______________ (leer) tú las tiras cómicas?

MARIO Claro que sí. A ver... durante el día, mi hermana Luisa y yo (5) ______________ (asistir) a una clase de ejercicios aeróbicos. Mis padres (6) ______________ (correr) por la playa y mis abuelos (7) ______________ (hacer) ejercicio en el gimnasio.

9 Patricia has written a short letter to her pen-pal about all of the activities going on this weekend. Complete this portion of her letter by filling in the blanks with the correct form of the verb in parentheses.

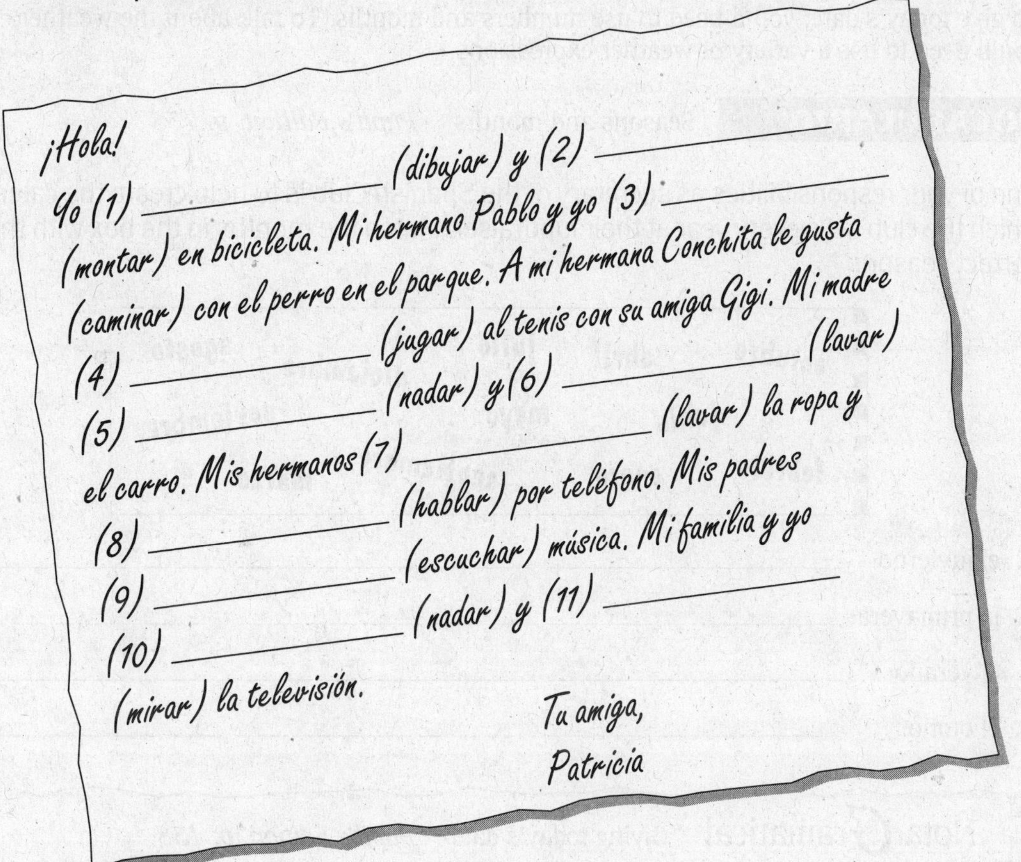

¡Hola!

Yo (1) ______________ (dibujar) y (2) ______________ (montar) en bicicleta. Mi hermano Pablo y yo (3) ______________ (caminar) con el perro en el parque. A mi hermana Conchita le gusta (4) ______________ (jugar) al tenis con su amiga Gigi. Mi madre (5) ______________ (nadar) y (6) ______________ (lavar) (lavar) la ropa y el carro. Mis hermanos (7) ______________ (hablar) por teléfono. Mis padres (8) ______________ (escuchar) música. Mi familia y yo (9) ______________ (nadar) y (10) ______________ (11) ______________ (mirar) la televisión.

Tu amiga,

Patricia

10 Ernesto and Maricarmen have surveyed their classmates to discover some of their typical weekend activities. Complete the students' sentences by deciding which verb fits best in the sentence. Then correctly conjugate the verb.

MODELO Luis <u>estudia</u> (estudiar, bailar) en la biblioteca.

1. Raimundo ______________ (escuchar, lavar) la ropa el sábado.
2. Simón y sus padres ______________ (hacer, cantar) ejercicio en el gimnasio.
3. Michelle ______________ (caminar, cuidar) a sus hermanos.
4. Felipe y yo ______________ (montar, regresar) en bicicleta.
5. Teresa ______________ (trabajar, bailar) en el supermercado.
6. Silvia y yo ______________ (pintar, caminar) con los perros.
7. Bernardo y Lupe ______________ (mirar, recibir) la televisión.
8. Soledad ______________ (asistir, leer) las tiras cómicas en el periódico.
9. Tú ______________ (nadar, escribir) cartas a unos amigos.
10. Yo ______________ (beber, bailar) jugo y ______________ (comer, cantar) un sándwich.

Nombre ______________________ Clase ____________ Fecha ____________

TERCER PASO

To give today's date, you'll need to use numbers and months. To talk about the weather, you'll need to use a variety of weather expressions.

VOCABULARIO Seasons and months *Pupil's Edition, p. 138*

11 One of your responsibilities as secretary of the Spanish Club is to help create the calendar which the club sells every year at their fundraiser. Match the months in the box with the correct season.

octubre abril julio diciembre agosto junio mayo noviembre febrero enero septiembre marzo

1. el invierno: ____________ ____________ ____________
2. la primavera: ____________ ____________ ____________
3. el verano: ____________ ____________ ____________
4. el otoño: ____________ ____________ ____________

Nota Gramatical Giving today's date *Pupil's Edition, p. 138*

Use the formula **el** + *number* **de** + *month* to give today's date. Use **el primero** for the first day. In Spanish the "on" is omitted in expressions like *on the sixth.*

Hoy es **el veinte de julio.** *Today is July 20th.*
La fiesta es **el diez.** *The party is on the tenth.*

12 Your friend from Spain wants to know when Conchita Martínez will be playing while on tour in the U. S. Write the dates of her tennis matches in Spanish.

1. January 25 ______________________
2. February 13 ______________________
3. March 18 ______________________
4. April 2 ______________________
5. May 15 ______________________
6. July 4 ______________________
7. September 7 ______________________
8. December 12 ______________________

13 You've volunteered to help prepare the newsletter for the Hispanic Chamber of Commerce. Your task is to prepare the list of the ten scheduled meetings for this year. In Spanish, write the dates for the following scheduled meetings.

1. January 8 ____
2. February 18 ____
3. March 11 ____
4. April 26 ____
5. May 19 ____
6. June 20 ____
7. July 5 ____
8. August 1 ____
9. September 14 ____
10. October 9 ____
11. November 30 ____
12. December 15 ____

14 Beth works in a very busy office! She's trying to schedule meetings around all the trips everyone will be taking for the next few months. In Spanish, write where each person is going and when he or she plans to leave.

MODELO María / Cancún / August 4 **María va a Cancún el cuatro de agosto.**

1. Peter / Los Ángeles / February 17 ____
2. Carol / New York City / March 23 ____
3. Pablo / Chicago / April 26 ____
4. Miguel y Bridget / Philadelphia / June 1 ____
5. Tú / Santiago de Chile / July 18 ____
6. Bárbara y Abby / Austin, Texas / September 6 ____
7. Yo / Denver / October 9 ____
8. Denise / Miami / November 16 ____

VOCABULARIO

Weather expressions *Pupil's Edition, p. 140*

15 It's Julio's first day as a weather forecaster and he's arrived late! Help him get ready for his appearance by matching the weather reports in the word box to the weather conditions for the cities listed below.

Hace frío.	**Hace fresco.**	**Nieva.**	**Está nublado.**
Hace mucho calor.	**Hace viento.**	**Llueve.**	**Hace sol.**

_______________ 1. a windy day in Chicago

_______________ 2. a bright, sunny day in San Diego

_______________ 3. a very hot afternoon in Phoenix

_______________ 4. a rainy morning in Seattle

_______________ 5. a cloudy day in Milwaukee

_______________ 6. a cool evening in Boston

_______________ 7. a snowy day in Aspen

_______________ 8. a cold morning in Minneapolis

16 Write a description of the weather in the following cities according to the illustrations.

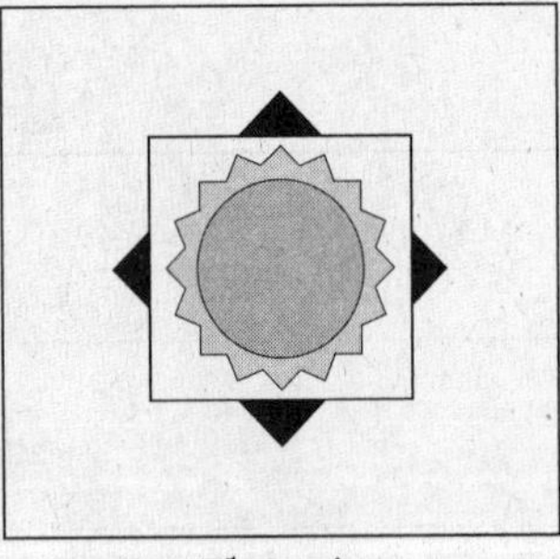

Phoenix

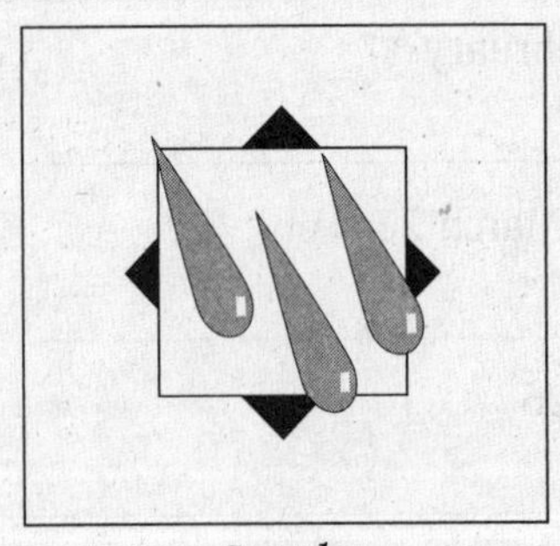

Seattle

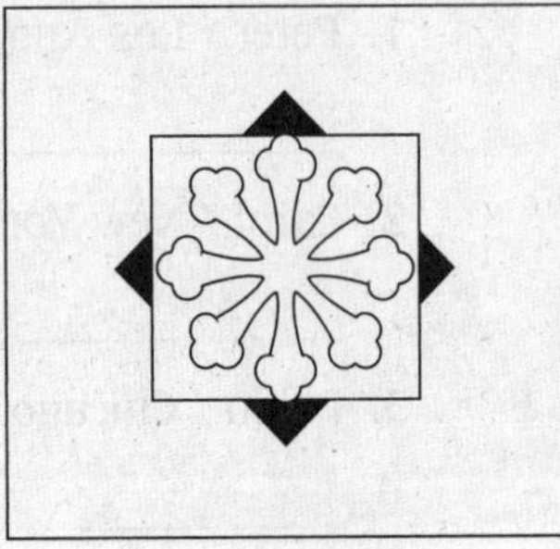

Minneapolis

1. En Phoenix _______________.
2. En Seattle _______________.
3. En Minneapolis _______________.

CAPÍTULO 6

Nombre ______________________ Clase ____________ Fecha ____________

Entre familia

PRIMER PASO

To describe your family, you'll need to know the names of family members and how to use possessive adjectives.

VOCABULARIO Family members *Pupil's Edition, p. 153*

1 Dwayne, an exchange student in La Paz, Bolivia, is describing his family members to his host family. Help with his descriptions by writing the correct family member in each blank below. Some of the choices can be used more than once.

1. La madre de mi madre es mi ______________________.
2. El hermano de mi madre es mi ______________________.
3. Mi hermana es la ______________________ de mis padres.
4. La hija de mi madre y mi padrastro es mi ______________________.
5. La madre de mi tío es mi ______________________.
6. La esposa de mi padre que no es mi madre es mi ______________________.

2 Look at the family tree and tell how these people are related to Ana.

Rebeca Martínez de Cohen – ❤ – Alberto Cohen

León Brodsky – ❤ – Susana Cohen de Brodsky　Esteban Cohen – ❤ – Maureen Hernández de Cohen

Rafael Brodsky　Arturo Brodsky　**Ana Brodsky**　Benjamín Cohen　David Cohen　Lynn Cohen

MODELO Rebeca Cohen **Es la abuela de Ana.**

1. Susana Brodsky ______________________
2. Alberto Cohen ______________________
3. Esteban Cohen ______________________
4. Arturo Brodsky ______________________
5. Maureen Hernández ______________________
6. León Brodsky ______________________
7. Rafael Brodsky ______________________

Nombre ______________________ Clase ______________ Fecha ______________

Nota Gramatical Possessive adjectives *Pupil's Edition, p. 154*

Pupil's Edition, p. 154

- You already know the singular possessive adjectives:
  mi(s) *(my)*, **tu(s)** *(your)*, and **su(s)** *(his, hers, your)*.
- The plural possessive adjectives are: **nuestro/a(s)** *(our)*, **vuestro/a(s)** *(your-* Spain*)*, and **su(s)** *(your, their)*.
  These adjectives agree in number with the nouns they modify.
  Nuestros amigos miran la televisión.
  Sus hermanas escuchan la radio.
- Remember that **nuestro** and **vuestro** also agree in gender with the nouns they are modifying.
  Silvia es nuestra hermana y nuestras primas son Eva y Julia.

3 Felipe invited some friends to his family reunion. Help him introduce his family members to his friends by circling the possessive adjective that correctly completes each sentence.

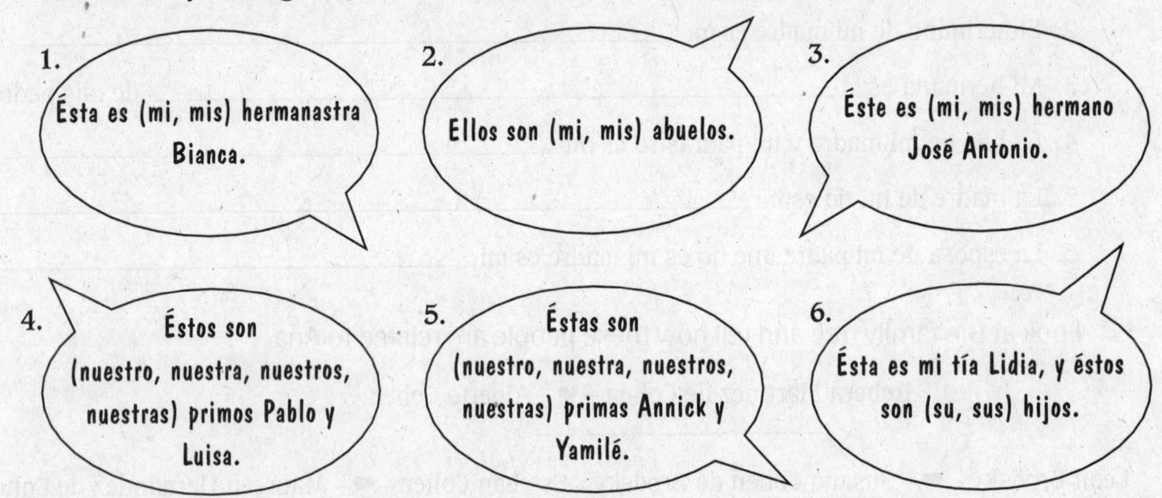

4 Alexis is on vacation with her family, but everyone misses something from home. Complete each of her sentences with the correct form of the possessive adjective.

1. Mis hermanos quieren ______________ tiras cómicas. No quieren leer novelas.
2. Yo quiero ______________ traje de baño *(bathing suit)* porque quiero nadar en el lago.
3. Marcos quiere ______________ radio porque quiere escuchar música.
4. Nosotros queremos ______________ videojuegos que están en casa.
5. Iris y Sandra quieren ______________ revistas que dejaron *(they left)* en casa.
6. Quiero ver a ______________ mejores amigos Sara y Felipe porque quiero hablar un poco con ellos.
7. Tú quieres ______________ zapatillas de tenis para jugar al tenis con Hana.
8. Mi hermana y yo queremos ______________ novelas porque no tenemos nada que leer.

CAPÍTULO 6 Primer paso

SEGUNDO PASO

To describe someone, you'll need to use decriptive words and expressions. To discuss activities a family can do together, you'll often need to use the verbs **hacer** and **salir** and the personal **a.**

VOCABULARIO

Descriptive words and expressions *Pupil's Edition, p. 158*

5 Liza and Lucas are twins. Complete each sentence with an appropriate adjective.

MODELO Liza es alta. → Lucas también es alto.

1. Liza es pelirroja y un poco gorda. Lucas también es ______ y un poco ______.
2. Liza es cariñosa. Lucas también es ______.
3. Lucas es muy listo. Liza también es muy ______.
4. Liza es traviesa. Lucas también es ______.
5. Lucas es atractivo. Liza también es ______.

6 Jani is writing a letter to her pen pal Zuri describing her friends. Fill in the blanks with the correct form of the adjective in parentheses.

Hola Zuri:

Mi amigo Guillermo es (1) ______ (bajo), con ojos (2) ______ (azul). Su hermana Cora también es (3) ______ (bajo), pero ella tiene ojos de color café. Sonja es (4) ______ (atractivo) y un poco (5) ______ (travieso). Megan es (6) ______ (pelirrojo) y tiene ojos (7) ______ (verde). Mi amigo Narciso es (8) ______ (alto) y muy (9) ______ (delgado). Sus hermanas, Anaba y Altsoba también son muy (10) ______ (alto).

Tu amiga,

Jani

Nombre ______________________ Clase ____________ Fecha ____________

7 Hiroshi and his sister Umeko never agree on anything! Read Hiroshi's descriptions of the following people, then rewrite the sentences the way Umeko would respond.

MODELO —La hermana de Steve es delgada.
—No es cierto. La hermana de Steve es un poco gorda.

1. —Francisco es muy joven.

   —No es cierto. ______________________.
2. —Helen es mayor que Lisa.

   —No es cierto. ______________________.
3. —Pablo es un poco gordo.

   —No es cierto. ______________________.
4. —Sofía tiene pelo negro.

   —No es cierto. ______________________.
5. —Éric tiene ojos de color café.

   —No es cierto. ______________________.

Nota *G*ramatical

The verbs **hacer** and **salir** *Pupil's Edition, p. 160*

- The verb **hacer** *(to make, to do)* is conjugated as follows:

yo	**hago**	nosotros	**hacemos**
tú	**haces**	vosotros	hacéis
él/ ella/ usted	**hace**	ellos/ ellas/ ustedes	**hacen**

- The verb **salir** *(to go out)* is conjugated as follows:

yo	**salgo**	nosotros	**salimos**
tú	**sales**	vosotros	salís
él/ ella/ usted	**sale**	ellos/ ellas/ ustedes	**salen**

8 Latwanda is describing what she and her friends do during the week. Fill in the blanks with the correct forms of **hacer** or **salir**.

1. Los lunes yo ______________ mi tarea antes de cenar.
2. Roy ______________ con sus amigos los viernes.
3. Torrence, Odessa y yo ______________ nuestra tarea juntos en la biblioteca.
4. Anthony, Marvella, y Sarah ______________ con sus amigos los sábados. Les gusta ver películas nuevas.
5. Batini casi nunca ______________ su tarea con nosotros porque siempre estudia sola *(alone)*.
6. Durante el invierno, mi familia y yo siempre ______________ un viaje a Aspen.
7. ¿ ______________ tú y tu familia algo durante el invierno?

9 Write the questions that would have caused Cindy to give the following responses:

1. ¿______________________________?
   Los lunes hago mi tarea antes de cenar.
2. ¿______________________________?
   En general, estudio en la biblioteca los sábados.
3. ¿______________________________?
   Sí, mi familia y yo hacemos un viaje todos los veranos.
4. ¿______________________________?
   Sí, Juan y Luisa salen juntos.

Nota Gramatical

Personal a — *Pupil's Edition, p. 161*

The personal **a** is used when the direct object is a person.

Visito **a** mi abuela en Francia todos los veranos.

When the direct object is a place or a thing, the **a** is not used.

Siempre visito la torre Eiffel cuando estoy en París.

10 Ernesto has written a letter to his friend Eli. Sometimes it is difficult to tell whether he is talking about a person, place or thing. Fill in the blanks where needed with the personal **a**. Mark an X in the blank if the sentence does not need a personal **a**.

Hola Eli:

Cada verano visito (1) ____________ mis abuelos en Miami. El viernes, voy a visitar (2) ____________ la Calle Ocho. Llamo (3) ____________ mis padres casi todos los sábados. Este domingo, voy a visitar (4) ____________ los Cayos de la Florida. Vamos a visitar (5) ____________ mis tíos que viven allí. Quiero conocer (6) ____________ la nueva esposa de mi tío Mario. Estoy tan ocupado que no tengo tiempo para mirar (7) ____________ la televisión o escuchar (8) ____________ la radio. Y tú, Eli, ¿cómo pasas (9) ____________ tus vacaciones?

Hasta pronto,

Ernesto

Nombre ______________________ Clase ______________ Fecha ______________

TERCER PASO

To discuss problems and give advice, you'll need to use the verb **deber**. You also may want to talk about household chores and use the verb **poner**.

Nota Gramatical The verb **deber** *Pupil's Edition, p. 164*

The verb **deber** *(should, ought to)* is conjugated as follows:

yo **debo**	nosotros **debemos**
tú **debes**	vosotros debéis
él/ ella/ usted **debe**	ellos/ ellas/ ustedes **deben**

11 Tamika and her friends are telling each other what they think people should do to lead a healthier life. Fill in each blank with the correct form of the verb **deber**.

TAMIKA Tú (1) ______________ practicar un deporte como la natación.

DESIRÉE Silvia (2) ______________ descansar más.

CARMEN Creo que Ann y Pedro no (3) ______________ trabajar tanto.

MIGUEL Sí, es cierto. Ellos (4) ______________ ir de vacaciones.

STANLEY Todos nosotros (5) ______________ pasar más tiempo con la familia y menos en la oficina.

12 Use **deber** and the phrases provided in the box to create five sentences about what these people should do become better students.

estudiar con los amigos · **hablar menos en clase** · **escuchar más al profesor** · **hacer toda la tarea** · **estudiar en la biblioteca** · **organizar los papeles**

1. Yo ______________________________
2. Tú ______________________________
3. Mi amigo ______________________________
4. Nosotros ______________________________
5. Ustedes ______________________________
6. Mis compañeros de clase ______________________________

VOCABULARIO Household chores *Pupil's Edition, p. 165*

13 Rearrange the letters in the boxes to reveal what chores everyone has to do.

1. Yo necesito [RTAORC LE ÉDECSP.] ______________
2. Manolo debe [NAARHCLP] su ropa. ______________
3. Liselotte quiere [MPIIARL AL IACNOC.] ______________
4. Juan va a [SAPAR AL DARORAIPAS] en la sala. ______________
5. Jamyce quiere [BRATARAJ NE LE DNARJÍ.] ______________
6. Federico necesita [CHAER AL MCAA.] ______________
7. Melissa va a [RACIUD LA TAGO] de su amigo Pablo. ______________
8. Dwan debe [NOPRE AL SAME] antes de cenar. ______________

14 You overhear Carlos and his friends talking about what they do to help out around the house. Fill in each blank with a correct verb to complete their conversation.

JEANNIE Todos los días, mi prima (1) ______________ la mesa antes de cenar.

CARLOS Después de comer, mi hermano Mikel y yo (2) ______________ la cocina.

FELIX Mis hermanas y yo no ayudamos en la cocina. Nosotros siempre (3) ______________ la ropa.

ANDRÉS Yo (4) ______________ en el jardín con mi papá.

KELLY Mi hermanastra Cathi (5) ______________ la aspiradora, pero yo (6) ______________ la cama.

15 Use the clues below to write a sentence about what each person needs to do tonight.

MODELO Hichem tiene dos gatos, Frijoles y Frankie.
Hichem debe cuidar a los gatos.

1. A mí me gusta plantar flores *(flowers)*.

   ____

2. Javier necesita arreglar *(to arrange)* su cuarto.

   ____

3. Mamá quiere trabajar afuera. *(outside)*

   ____

4. Don va a limpiar la sala.

   ____

5. Tú quieres vestirte *(dress)* bien mañana.

   ____

Nombre ______________________ Clase ____________ Fecha ____________

Nota Gramatical hacer, salir, and poner *Pupil's Edition, p. 165*

The present tense of **hacer, salir,** and **poner** is regular in all but the **yo** form:

yo	**hago**	**salgo**	**pongo**
tú	haces	sales	pones
él, ella, usted	hace	sale	pone
nosotros	hacemos	salimos	ponemos
vosotros	hacéis	salís	ponéis
ellos, ellas, ustedes	hacen	salen	ponen

16 Change the following sentences to agree with each new subject.

1. Marcos hace la cama antes de salir.

   Tú ______________________ cuando regresas.
2. Nosotros salimos juntos los viernes.

   Wei y Cristina nunca ______________________.
3. Los muchachos ponen la mesa los lunes y los jueves.

   Yo ______________________ los fines de semana.
4. Édgar hace la tarea antes de mirar la televisión.

   Julieta y yo ______________________ por la mañana.
5. Rikki sale con Mark y Rebecca.

   Yo ______________________ con Pablo y María.
6. Yo pongo la ropa en el armario.

   Ustedes ______________________ en una canasta *(basket)*.

17 Conjugate the verbs to create sentences about what these people do on the weekend.

1. Jimmy / poner / la ropa / en el armario

   ____
2. Mis amigas y yo / salir / todos los sábados

   ____
3. Tú / siempre / poner / la mesa / en casa

   ____
4. Lorna / hacer / la tarea / en la biblioteca

   ____
5. Sanjay y Ajai / hacer / la cama / en su cuarto

   ____

CAPÍTULO 6 Tercer paso

Nombre ______________________ Clase __________ Fecha __________

CAPÍTULO 7

¿Qué te gustaría hacer?

PRIMER PASO

To talk on the telephone and to extend and accept invitations, you'll need to use stem-changing verbs. You'll also need to know the names for various places around town.

ASÍ SE DICE Talking on the telephone *Pupil's Edition, p. 183*

1 Norman is trying to call his friend Dorotea. Choose the most logical expressions from the word box to complete the dialogue between Norman and Dorotea's mother.

momento	Aló	ocupada	llamo más tarde
un recado	Sí, está bien	De parte de quién	

SEÑORA ¿ (1) ______________________?

NORMAN Buenos días. ¿Está Dorotea, por favor?

SEÑORA ¿ (2) ______________________?

NORMAN De parte de Norman Armani.

SEÑORA Un (3) ______________________... Lo siento, Dorotea no está.

NORMAN Gracias. ¿Puedo dejar (4) ______________________?

SEÑORA (5) ______________________.

2 What would you say...

1. when you answer the telephone?

____

2. when the line is busy?

____

3. to ask to leave a message?

____

4. to say you'll call back later?

____

5. to ask who's calling?

____

Gramática e → ie stem-changing verbs *Pupil's Edition, p. 185*

- In **e → ie** stem-changing verbs, the letter **e** in the stem changes to **ie** in all forms except the **nosotros** and **vosotros** forms. Look at the way the stem changes in the verb **empezar** *(to begin)*:

yo empiezo	nosotros empezamos
tú empiezas	vosotros empezáis
él / ella / usted empieza	ellos / ellas / ustedes empiezan

- Some stem-changing verbs have an irregular **-go** in the **yo** form. These verbs usually don't have a stem-change in the **yo** form. Two examples are **tener** and **venir**:

TENER		VENIR	
tengo	tenemos	vengo	venimos
tienes	tenéis	vienes	venís
tiene	tienen	viene	vienen

3 Aïcha and her friends are talking about their activities. Fill in each blank with the correct form of the verb in parentheses.

AÏCHA ¡Mi clase de baile **(1)** ______ (empezar) esta noche!

JOSÉ No me gusta bailar, yo **(2)** ______ (preferir) cantar.

SHAUNA Mi hermana Eva canta en un coro. Ella **(3)** ______ (tener) una voz buena.

FREDDY Nosotros **(4)** ______ (querer) asistir a un concierto cuando ella canta.

SHAUNA Bueno, va a cantar en mi casa mañana para el cumpleaños de mi tío Reggie. ¿Ustedes **(5)** ______ (venir) mañana? Es a las siete.

4 Combine the elements given to create sentences. Then answer the questions that follow.

1. **a.** Juan / preferir / jugar / al tenis **b.** ¿Y tú? ¿A qué prefieres jugar?
   a. ______
   b. ______
2. **a.** Marisa / venir / a / clase / a las ocho **b.** ¿Y tú? ¿A qué hora vienes a clase?
   a. ______
   b. ______
3. **a.** Ellie y Juan / querer / hacer ejercicio / en el gimnasio **b.** ¿Dónde quieres hacer ejercicio tú?
   a. ______
   b. ______
4. **a.** Nosotras / tener / un amigo / muy travieso **b.** ¿Y tú? ¿Tienes un amigo travieso?
   a. ______
   b. ______

VOCABULARIO Places and events *Pupil's Edition, p. 186*

5 Unscramble the items below. Then tell whether each item is an event **(evento)** or a place **(lugar)** by circling the correct word.

1. LE SEUOM ED GOANOPLTROÍA ______________ evento lugar
2. AL EFIAST ED PARSREOS ______________ evento lugar
3. LE GOOCLÓZIO ______________ evento lugar
4. AL DOAB ______________ evento lugar
5. AL SEIATF ED MUPELOAÑSC ______________ evento lugar
6. LE UEARPQ ED CARCTEOINSEA ______________ evento lugar

6 Match the places on the right with their descriptions on the left.

_____ 1. Aquí ves las obras de teatro de Shakespeare.
_____ 2. En este lugar hay animales exóticos.
_____ 3. Aquí ves a unos acróbatas.
_____ 4. En este lugar hay muchos edificios altos y grandes.
_____ 5. Aquí hay unos peces *(fish)* tropicales.

a. el circo
b. el acuario
c. el parque de atracciones
d. el teatro
e. el zoológico
f. la ciudad

7 Luisa, an Ecuadorean exchange student, is writing a letter to her mother about her trip to Atlanta, Georgia. Fill in each blank with the correct vocabulary word.

circo ciudad zoológico lago campo acuario parque de atracciones

Querida mamá,

¡Me gusta mucho la (1) ______________ de Atlanta! Me gusta más que nada el (2) ______________, donde puedes ver los elefantes, las cebras, y los rinocerontes. El 20 de noviembre vamos al (3) ______________ de Chattanooga, Tennessee, para ver los peces exóticos que tienen allí. El (4) ______________ va a venir a Atlanta este fin de semana. Estoy muy contenta porque quiero ver a los gimnastas de trapecio. La mayoría del tiempo vamos al (5) ______________ para montar en bicicleta o al (6) ______________ de Cartersville para pescar.

SEGUNDO PASO

To make plans, you'll need to use the verb **pensar** and the structure **ir + a** + infinitive. To talk about getting ready, you'll need to know reflexive verbs.

Nota Gramatical The verb **pensar** *Pupil's Edition, p. 188*

The stem-changing verb **pensar** is used before an infinitive to mean *to plan* or *to intend* to do something. It is conjugated as follows:

yo pienso	nosotros / nosotras pensamos
tú piensas	vosotros / vosotras pensáis
él / ella / usted piensa	ellos / ellas / ustedes piensan

8 Mr. Porter is asking some students about what they're planning to do this weekend. Complete their answers by filling in the blanks with the correct forms of **pensar.**

MELI Yo (1) _______________ estudiar para mi examen de geometría.

LORRAINE Mis hermanas y yo (2) _______________ visitar a nuestros abuelos.

JEREMY Mi amigo Enrique (3) _______________ ir al cine pero yo no voy con él.

ALECCA Mis primos (4) _______________ dar una fiesta para celebrar el aniversario de mi tío Juan y mi tía Kate. Voy a celebrar con ellos.

BENJAMÍN Voy al zoológico con mis padres. Meli, tú (5) _______________ ir con nosotros, ¿no?

LANIE El domingo por la tarde voy al teatro para ver *La casa de Bernarda Alba.* Y ustedes, ¿qué (6) _______________ hacer?

9 Use the subjects given, the verb **pensar,** and the expressions in the box below to create sentences about what people intend to do this spring break.

asistir a una fiesta **ir al teatro** **ir al lago** **visitar el acuario** **dar una fiesta de cumpleaños** **ir al museo de antropología** **estudiar en el parque**

1. Nosotros ____.
2. Tú ____.
3. Mi amigo Juan ____.
4. Mis amigas(os) ____.
5. Yo ____.
6. Ustedes ____.

Nota Gramatical ir + a + infinitive *Pupil's Edition, p. 188*

The verb **ir** is used before an infinitive to talk about what someone is going to do in the future. **Ir** is always linked to the infinitive by the preposition **a.**

Martín **va a trabajar** mañana. *Martin is going to work tomorrow.*

Yo **voy a visitar** a mi abuela. *I'm going to visit my grandmother.*

10 Yori is writing a letter to his friend, Sam, about what he and his friends are going to do in the future. Complete his letter with the correct forms of **ir.**

... En el futuro, yo (1) ______ a trabajar para el ejército como piloto de helicópteros. Mi hermana Hana (2) ______ a ser ingeniera mecánica para trabajar en una compañía de computadoras. Este verano nosotros (3) ______ a asistir a un campo de ciencias para aprender más sobre estas profesiones. Mis amigas Cristina y Ema (4) ______ a ser doctoras. Mi amigo Jo (5) ______ a tomar clases porque quiere ser profesor de historia. ¿Y tú, Sam? ¿Qué (6) ______ a hacer tú en el futuro? ¿Qué (7) ______ a estudiar tus amigos? ...

11 Estrella's friends are creatures of habit! The following paragraph describes what they're doing this week. Change the underlined verbs to describe what each person is going to do next week. The first one has been done for you.

Mi hermano Esteban y yo **(1)** nadamos en la piscina de nuestra tía Luisa. Después de nadar, yo **(2)** cuido a mis primos porque Luisa trabaja por la tarde. Clara **(3)** mira la televisión y su hermano Claude **(4)** lee una revista. Aaron y David **(5)** pasan el rato con sus amigas en el parque. Greta y Kenesha **(6)** practican los deportes en el gimnasio. Sandra y Alfredo **(7)** juegan al voleibol con sus hermanitos. Nosotros todos **(8)** estudiamos antes de dormir.

1. **vamos a nadar**
2. ______
3. ______
4. ______
5. ______
6. ______
7. ______
8. ______

Nota Gramatical Reflexive verbs *Pupil's Edition, p. 190*

- Reflexive verbs have two parts: a verb form and a reflexive pronoun.
  Cuando vas a la escuela, ¿te gusta maquillarte?
- The reflexive pronoun refers to the subject of the sentence and indicates that the action is being done to oneself.
  Éric va a afeitarse. *Eric is going to shave.*

12 Vanya and Mateo have been interviewed about their morning routine. Read their responses and underline all of the reflexive verbs you see. Then answer the questions that follow.

VANYA

A las seis y media, necesito ducharme. A las siete menos veinticinco, necesito ponerme la ropa y peinarme. A las siete menos cuarto, siempre necesito lavarme los dientes y maquillarme.

MATEO

Tengo que levantarme a las siete. Después de levantarme siempre necesito ducharme. Después necesito afeitarme y peinarme. Luego, necesito ponerme la ropa. Después de desayunar, necesito lavarme los dientes.

1. Who takes a shower at 6:30? ______________________
2. Who gets dressed before styling his or her hair? ______________________
3. What does Vanya need to do to get ready for school that Mateo doesn't list?
   ____
4. What does Mateo need to do to get ready for school that Vanya doesn't list?
   ____

13 Say what each person is going to do, based on the clues provided.

MODELO Ernesto va a usar el jabón y el agua. **Ernesto va a ducharse.**

1. Luis necesita una navaja y la crema de afeitar.
   ____
2. Yo necesito un cepillo de dientes y la pasta de dientes.
   ____
3. Tú vas a llevar la ropa y las zapatillas de tenis.
   ____
4. Mónica va a usar el maquillaje.
   ____

TERCER PASO

To turn down an invitation or make an excuse, you'll need to use some new expressions. You'll also need to use the verb **tener.**

Turning down an invitation and making an excuse *Pupil's Edition, p. 193*

14 Unscramble the following elements to find out what excuses Sammy's friends gave for not being able to go bicycling with him.

1. lástima / planes / ya / qué / tengo
______
2. siento / estoy / lo / ocupado / esta / noche
______
3. puedo / pero / no / me / gustaría
______
4. un / enfermo / cansado / estoy / y / poco
______
5. siento / vez / tal / día / otro / lo
______
6. lástima / estoy / qué / pero / ocupado
______

15 Nadema is looking for someone to go horseback riding with her tonight. Unfortunately, none of her friends is able to go. Read about each person's situation and then explain why she or he can't go.

1. Laura va a una fiesta de cumpleaños con sus padres.
______
2. Sofía va al cine con su novio Eduardo.
______
3. Moufida trabajó *(worked)* todo el día.
______
4. Rudy tiene fiebre *(a fever).*
______
5. Jamal va a hacer su tarea esta noche.
______

Nota *G*ramatical Expressions with **tener** *Pupil's Edition, p. 193*

The following are some expressions with **tener**:

tener ganas de + infinitive *to feel like (doing something)*

Mónica **tiene ganas de** jugar al fútbol.

tener prisa *to be in a hurry*

Tengo prisa porque mi clase empieza a las ocho en punto.

tener que + infinitive *to have to (do something)*

Silvio **tiene que** ayudar en casa esta noche.

tener sueño *to be sleepy*

Enrique no descansa mucho. Ahora **tiene sueño.**

16 Manuel and his friends are discussing why they can't go to the zoo with Enrique this weekend. Fill in the blanks in their conversation with **que, sueño, prisa,** or **ganas**.

MANUEL Oye Manolo, ¿por qué no vas al cine con Luisa y Renaldo?

MANOLO Lo siento hombre, pero yo tengo **(1)** ______________________ hacer la tarea.

DANA Yo también. Siempre tengo mucha **(2)** ______________________. No tengo tiempo para salir con mis amigos.

ISABEL Y la realidad es que yo no tengo **(3)** ______________________ de ir al zoológico. Prefiero ir al teatro con mi amiga Raquel.

TYRONE Yo tengo mucho **(4)** ______________________. No descanso nada. Voy a descansar este fin de semana.

17 You're filling out a survey about the things that people have to do. Answer the following questions using the new phrases you've learned in this chapter.

1. ¿Qué tienes que hacer para estar listo(a) por la mañana?

____

2. ¿Qué tienen que hacer los estudiantes para recibir una "A" en su clase de español?

____

3. ¿Qué tienes ganas de hacer esta noche con tu familia?

____

4. ¿Tienes prisa por la mañana? ¿Por qué?

____

5. ¿Qué tiene ganas de hacer tu mejor amigo con su familia este fin de semana?

____

6. ¿Tienes sueño ahora? ¿Por qué?

____

Nombre ______________________ Clase __________ Fecha __________

¡A comer!

PRIMER PASO

To talk about meals and food, you'll need to use food vocabulary and the verb **encantar.**

VOCABULARIO Breakfast foods *Pupil's Edition, p. 207*

1 Silvia is working in her uncle's café. Help her with some breakfast orders by identifying in Spanish the items listed.

1. toast ______________________
2. pineapple ______________________
3. grapefruit ______________________
4. bacon ______________________
5. banana ______________________
6. eggs ______________________
7. milk ______________________

2 Luis and Mónica are trying to create three different menus for their brunch next Sunday. Help them out by filling in three items for each menu listed below.

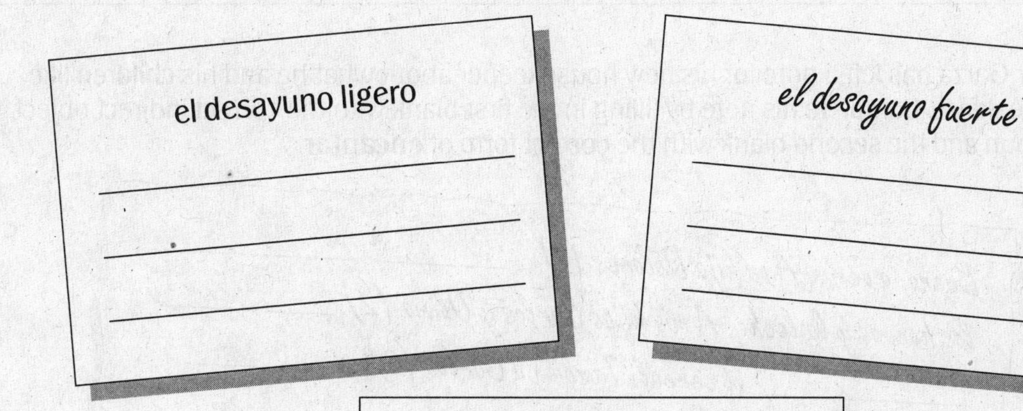

el desayuno ecuatoriano

____

____

____

Gramática encantar and indirect object pronouns *Pupil's Edition, p. 208*

- The verb **encantar** *(to really like; to love)* is similar to the verb **gustar.**

  Me encanta el pan tostado y a Luis **le encantan** los huevos.

  Te encanta el programa de televisión y **nos encantan** las películas.

  A Eva y Juan **les encanta** cantar y a usted **le encanta** cantar también, ¿no?

- The pronouns in front of the forms of **encantar** are indirect object prounouns. Indirect object pronouns tell *to whom* or *for whom* something is done. When used with **gustar** or **encantar,** they tell *to whom* something is pleasing.

  Te encanta la música rock, ¿no?
  You like rock music, right? (Rock music is pleasing to you, right?)

3 César is talking about his friends on the phone with his grandmother. Complete César's part of their conversation with the correct forms of the verb **encantar**.

Bueno, abuela, a Rubén le **(1)** ______________ ir al lago los domingos con su familia. A mis amigos Pablo y Miguel les **(2)** ______________ jugar al tenis los fines de semana. A Sofía le **(3)** ______________ las clases de aeróbicos en el gimnasio. A mí me **(4)** ______________ el zoológico porque hay unos animales allí. A todos nosotros nos **(5)** ______________ el parque de atracciones porque es muy divertido. Y a ti, abuela, te **(6)** ______________ visitar a tus amigos que viven en el campo, ¿verdad?

4 Señor Garza has left a note for his new housekeeper about what he and his children like for breakfast. Complete his note by filling in the first blank with the correct indirect object pronoun and the second blank with the correct form of **encantar**.

Bueno, a ver... A mi hija Dolores (1) __________ __________ los huevos y la leche. A mis hijos Carlos y Olivia (2) __________ __________ el cereal. También a Carlos (3) __________ __________ el tocino. A mí (4) __________ __________ el café y el pan dulce. A todos nosotros (5) __________ __________ los plátanos y los mangos, pero sólo a mi hija Sandra (6) __________ __________ la piña. Y a ti, (7) ¿__________ __________ el desayuno como a nosotros?

VOCABULARIO

Lunch foods *Pupil's Edition, p. 209*

5 Carlota has typed the lunch menu on the computer at her family's restaurant, but the computer scrambled the letters of all of the items! Can you figure out what they're serving today?

1. aodlnami ____________
2. haeculg ____________
3. usoeq ____________
4. itpsaap ____________
5. aannazm ____________
6. orerp telenaci ____________
7. aops ed mregusble ____________
8. cnwisádh ed aójnm ____________
9. sauv ____________
10. ét oríf ____________

6 You're working in a Spanish café for a summer job. Fill in the menu with appropriate foods and beverages.

sándwich de atún limonada papaya sándwich de queso manzana leche mango sopa de pollo té frío uvas sándwich de crema de maní y jalea piña sopa de legumbres sándwich de jamón toronja

SÁNDWICHES

____
____
____

FRUTAS

____
____
____

BEBIDAS

____
____
____

SOPAS

____
____
____

Gramática **o → ue** stem-changing verbs *Pupil's Edition, p. 210*

Almorzar *(to eat lunch)* and **poder** *(to be able, can)* are **o → ue** stem-changing verbs. Remember that the vowel **o** in stem-changing verbs changes to **ue** in all forms except **nosotros** and **vosotros.**

ALMORZAR		PODER	
almuerzo	almorzamos	puedo	podemos
almuerzas	almorzáis	puedes	podéis
almuerza	almuerzan	puede	pueden

7 Señor Kim runs a very popular lunch stand in New York City. He was recently interviewed by the local newspaper to find out when he and his customers eat lunch. Fill in the blanks with the correct forms of **almorzar.**

— ¿A qué hora **(1)** ______________ la gente?

— Bueno, el Sr. Rivera, un hombre muy simpático, siempre **(2)** ______________ a las doce en punto. ¡Siempre pide un perro caliente! Úrsula y Frida, dos mujeres que trabajan muy cerca, **(3)** ______________ a los dos.

— ¿Y usted? ¿Cuándo **(4)** ______________?

— Yo siempre **(5)** ______________ a las once. Mi esposa y yo **(6)** ______________ juntos todos los días.

8 Clara is trying to plan a lunch gathering for you. Answer her questions to help decide the best time to have lunch.

1. ¿A qué hora almuerzas?

____

2. En general, ¿qué almuerzas?

____

____

3. En general, ¿qué almuerzan tus padres?

____

____

4. ¿A qué hora almuerza tu mejor amigo(a)?

____

____

5. ¿Dónde almuerzan tú y tu familia los fines de semana?

____

Nombre ______________________ Clase ____________ Fecha ____________

SEGUNDO PASO

To comment on food, you'll need to use the verbs **ser** and **estar,** and you'll have occasions to use the idioms **tener sed** and **tener hambre.**

Nota Gramatical Using **ser** or **estar** with foods *Pupil's Edition, p. 212*

- Use **estar** to say how something tastes, looks, or feels.

  El tocino **está** rico. *The bacon is (tastes) delicious.*

  La salsa **está** picante. *The sauce is (tastes) spicy.*

- Use **ser** to say what something is like or to describe the general nature of something.

  Las uvas **son** ricas. *Grapes are delicious.*

  La pimienta **es** picante. *Pepper is spicy.*

9 Fernando is wondering what to order at the restaurant and he overhears people talking around him. Circle **a** if the customer he overhears is talking about how something *tastes,* or **b** if the customer is talking about *the general nature* of the food.

a b 1. El sándwich de jamón es muy salado.

a b 2. La sopa de pollo está rica.

a b 3. Los huevos están muy deliciosos.

a b 4. La leche está caliente.

a b 5. El tocino y el atún son salados.

a b 6. Los perros calientes están fríos.

10 Cecilia is working as a waitress at Lupe's Diner. Choose the most logical completion for what Cecilia tells her customers about the food.

1. "El té ____________ frío hoy."
   a. está **b.** es
2. "Las papitas ____________ buenas hoy."
   a. están **b.** son
3. "La limonada ____________ dulce hoy."
   a. está **b.** es
4. "El tocino ____________ delicioso hoy."
   a. está **b.** es
5. "Las papayas ____________ muy dulces por lo general."
   a. están **b.** son

CAPÍTULO 8 Segundo paso

Nota *G*ramatical — More expressions with **tener** *Pupil's Edition, p. 213*

The following are new expressions with **tener**:
tener sed *(to be thirsty)* and **tener hambre** *(to be hungry)*

Bárbara quiere un vaso de agua porque **tiene sed.**
Barbara wants a glass of water because she's thirsty.

Miguel quiere una hamburguesa porque **tiene hambre.**
Miguel wants a hamburger because he's hungry.

11 Berta and her friends have met for lunch. Complete each description with the correct form of **tener sed** or **tener hambre.**

1. Yo no ______________________. No quiero comer nada. Pero, quiero beber té porque ______________________.
2. Enrique quiere un sándwich porque ______________________.
3. Margarita y Luis quieren agua porque ______________________.
4. ¿______________________ tú? Hay limonada y jugo de piña.
5. ¡Guadalupe y Pepe ______________________! Van a comer ensalada, sopa de pollo, perros calientes y unas manzanas.

12 Read the following people's statements and then decide which **tener** expression would best describe each situation.

sed	sueño	prisa	ganas de	que	hambre

1. Julia y Raquel quieren tomar un litro de agua porque trabajan afuera hoy.
   Julia y Raquel tienen ______________.
2. Luis siempre tiene prisa. A veces no puede almorzar. Ahora son las cinco de la tarde.
   Luis tiene ______________.
3. La clase empieza a las ocho. Son las ocho menos diez y Esteban todavía está en casa.
   Esteban tiene ______________.
4. Ya es muy tarde. Ahora Elisabeth está cansada.
   Elisabeth tiene ______________.
5. La madre de Alonzo dice que él debe limpiar su cuarto para salir con sus amigos el viernes.
   Alonzo tiene ______________ limpiar su cuarto.

CAPÍTULO 8 Segundo paso

Nombre ______________________ Clase __________ Fecha __________

TERCER PASO

To make polite requests, order dinner, and ask for and pay the bill in a restaurant, you'll need to refer to foods and utensils and use the numbers 200 to 100,000.

VOCABULARIO

Utensils *Pupil's Edition, p. 216*

13 Marty is teaching his little cousin Claude which utensil to use for different foods. Help Marty out by completing each phrase with the correct utensil from the word box.

un vaso · un tazón · una servilleta · un cuchillo · un tenedor · un plato · una cuchara

1. Cuando bebo leche, uso ______________________.
2. Cuando como sopa, uso ______________________.
3. Cuando como ensalada, uso ______________________.
4. Cuando como pizza, siempre necesito ______________________.
5. Cuando como huevos, uso ______________________.
6. Cuando como helado, uso ______________________.
7. Cuando como un bistec *(a steak)*, uso ______________________.

14 Solve the following riddles using the new vocabulary.

1. Me usas *(You use me)* para cortar la comida. ______________________
2. Me usas cuando quieres beber algo. ______________________
3. Pones la comida sobre mí. ______________________
4. Me usas para comer la sopa. ______________________
5. Pones la sopa dentro de mí. ______________________
6. Me usas para limpiarte la cara *(face)*. ______________________

15 Sumi is serving brunch for her friends. Write the letter(s) in the blank of all the utensils that Sumi's guests would use to eat her brunch items.

a. la cuchara	1. ______ el pan tostado
b. el tenedor	2. ______ la leche
c. el plato	3. ______ el cereal
d. la servilleta	4. ______ huevos y tocino
e. el tazón	5. ______ la toronja
f. el vaso	6. ______ el jugo de naranja

CAPÍTULO 8 Tercer paso

Nota *G*ramatical otro *Pupil's Edition, p. 216*

The following are the forms of **otro** *(other, another)*: **otro, otra, otros, otras**

Quiero **otra** servilleta. *I want another napkin.*

Necesito **otro** vaso. *I need another glass.*

Mónica quiere **otras** uvas. *Mónica wants different grapes.*

Voy a pedir **otros** frijoles. *I'm going to ask for other beans.*

16 You're babysitting Brian, a five-year-old who always seems hungry. Fill in the blanks in his statements with the correct form of **otro.**

1. Yo quiero ____________________ vaso de leche, por favor.
2. Necesito ____________________ mango.
3. ¿Me puedes dar ____________________ ensalada?
4. Quiero ____________________ papitas y ____________________ sándwich de jamón.
5. Me gustaría ____________________ plátano para el cereal.
6. Me gustaría ____________________ perro caliente, por favor.
7. Quiero ____________________ toronja.
8. Me gustaría ____________________ manzana.

17 Camby is working at a delicatessen. Her customers are always asking for items they want or need. Unscramble the following elements to write what they might say to request various things.

1. de / limonada / otro / vaso / quiero

   ____

2. hermano / necesita / servilleta / otra / mi

   ____

3. sopa / gustaría / nos / otro / tazón / pollo / de / de

   ____

4. leche / café / quiero / otro / con

   ____

5. refresco / otro / amigo / mi / quiere

   ____

6. ¿tenedor / otro / por / favor / trae / me?

   ____

7. ¿plato / nos / fruta / puede / de / otro / traer?

   ____

CAPÍTULO 8 Tercer paso

VOCABULARIO Dinner foods *Pupil's Edition, p. 217*

18 For each group of three food items listed below, write the item that doesn't belong.

____________	1. el bistec	la cebolla	la carne de res
____________	2. el flan	el agua mineral	el café
____________	3. las zanahorias	la cebolla	el batido de fresa
____________	4. los camarones	la leche	el café
____________	5. el pescado	el pastel	el helado

19 Can you guess the food items that Pablo is describing below?

1. una bebida blanca ____________
2. una fruta verde o roja ____________
3. una legumbre anaranjada ____________
4. un postre muy frío ____________
5. una fruta amarilla de las zonas tropicales ____________
6. un líquido caliente que tomo con una cuchara ____________
7. una bebida caliente que bebes con el desayuno ____________
8. una comida con una parte blanca y otra parte amarilla ____________

VOCABULARIO Numbers 200 - 100,000 *Pupil's Edition, p. 219*

20 Look at the following series of numbers and write the number that would follow in each sequence.

MODELO 100, 300, 500, 700 **novecientos**

1. 200, 400, 600, 800, ____________
2. 400, 800, 1200, 1600, ____________
3. 500, 700, 900, 1.100, ____________
4. 600, 800, 1.100, 1.500, ____________
5. 750, 1.000, 1.250, 1.500, ____________

21 Write the answers to the following math problems in word form.

MODELO Quinientos más doscientos son **setecientos.**

1. Seiscientos menos doscientos son ____________
2. Cuatrocientos más trescientos son ____________
3. Setecientos más trescientos son ____________
4. Mil más quinientos son ____________
5. Diez mil más veinte mil son ____________

CAPÍTULO 9

Nombre ______________________ Clase ____________ Fecha ____________

¡Vamos de compras!

PRIMER PASO

To make suggestions for gifts, you'll need to use specific vocabulary and indirect object pronouns. To ask for and give directions around town, you'll need to know the names of various places.

VOCABULARIO Gift items *Pupil's Edition, p. 237*

1 Yasmina is looking for birthday gifts for her friend, Eloy. Decode these words using the clues given. Then use your responses to figure out what gift Yasmina is buying.

1. You wear this with a suit. ___ ___ ___ ___ ___ ___ ___ (8 24 5 4 9 20 9)
2. You wear these on your ears. ___ ___ ___ ___ ___ ___ (9 5 17 20 17 6)
3. You play this in your stereo. ___ ___ ___ ___ ___ (3 2 6 8 24)
___ ___ ___ ___ ___ ___ ___ ___ (8 24 22 10 9 8 20 24)
4. Its leaves are usually green. ___ ___ ___ ___ ___ ___ (10 1 9 19 20 9)
5. You play this with your family or friends. ___ ___ ___ ___ ___ ___ ___ (18 15 17 16 24 3 17)
___ ___ ___ ___ (22 17 6 9)

Yasmina is buying:

___ ___ ___ ___ ___ ___ ___ ___ ___ ___ (15 19 9 8 9 5 20 17 5 9)

2 Lois is shopping for gifts for her family. Suggest a gift she could buy for each one.

1. Su papá trabaja en una oficina muy formal. ______________________
2. A su abuela le encantan las rosas. ______________________
3. A su hermano Raúl le gusta la música rock. ______________________
4. Su hermanita Felicia tiene cinco años y le encanta jugar. ______________________
5. A su mamá le gustan las joyas *(jewelry)* elegantes. ______________________
6. Su primo Paco prefiere cosas sencillas como poemas o cartas. ______________________
7. A sus primos les gusta comer chocolate. ______________________
8. A sus tíos les gusta pasar el tiempo con su familia en casa. ______________________

*G*ramática Indirect object pronouns *Pupil's Edition, p. 238*

Indirect object pronouns tell *to whom* or *for whom* something is intended.

- Indirect object pronouns may come before a conjugated verb or attached to an infinitive.

  Le voy a dar el libro a Pablo. *I'm going to give the book to Pablo.*

  Voy a dar**le** la mochila a Ernesto. *I'm going to give the backpack to Ernesto.*

- **Le** can mean *to him, to her,* or *to you* (singular, formal). **Les** can mean *to them* or *to you* (plural). To clarify **le** or **les**, you can add the phrase **a** + *noun* or **a** + *pronoun.*

  Les compro las corbatas **a Juan** y **a Rafael.**
  I'm buying the ties for Juan and Rafael.

  ¿Quieres regalar**les** el disco compacto **a tus padres**?
  Do you want to give the CD to your parents?

3 Read the following conversation between Lourdes and some of her friends. Circle the indirect object pronouns and draw an arrow to the indirect objects they stand for.

LOURDES A mí me gusta ir de compras. Es muy divertido comprar regalos para mi familia y mis amigos.

FELIPE Estoy de acuerdo. Voy a darle unos dulces a mi tía Luisa. A ella le encantan.

LOURDES Yo quiero regalarle un disco compacto a mi mamá. Su música favorita es la música clásica.

WAN Yo voy a regalarle una planta a mi hermana. A ella le encanta cultivar *(to grow)* cosas.

JOSUÉ A mis hermanas les encantan las orquídeas *(orchids)*. Les quiero regalar unas flores tropicales a ellas.

4 Selena is talking to her friend Sofía about lunch with her family at a local restaurant. Read her statements, and fill in the blanks with the correct indirect object pronoun.

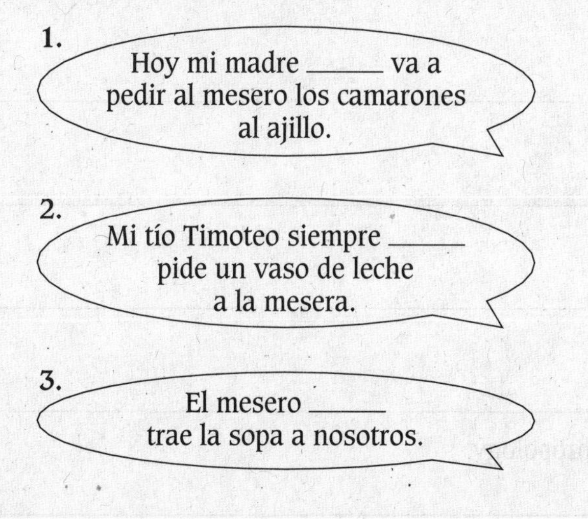

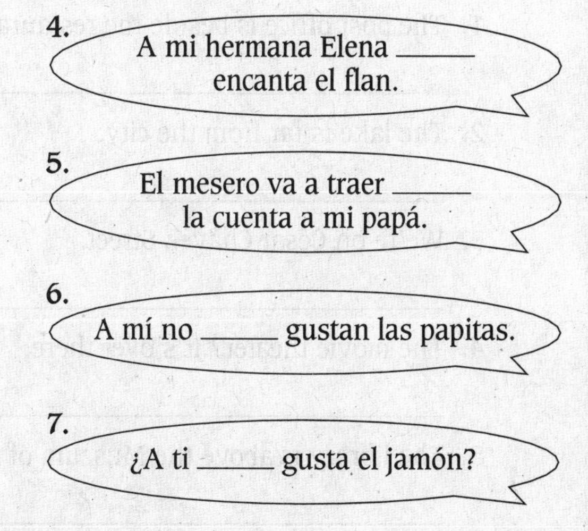

5 Rearrange the following elements to create sentences about what the following people want to give their friends and family.

1. queremos / a / nuestras / amigas / nosotros / unas / les / flores / regalar

____

____

2. ¿ le / comprar / tu / a / padre / qué / vas / a ?

____

____

3. Brenda / quiere / les / libros / no / a / ellos / dar / sus

____

____

4. van / una / corbata / a / ustedes / a / comprar / Joaquín / le

____

____

5. las / dar / a / juguetes / a / muchachas / le / unos / Mario / van

____

____

¿Te acuerdas? estar + location *Pupil's Edition, p. 239*

Estar is used to tell location. It is often used with the following prepositions of location:

al lado de *(next to)*
allá *(there)*
aquí *(here)*
cerca de *(near)*
debajo de *(under, beneath)*
encima de *(on top of)*
lejos de *(far from)*

6 Martina works for a tourism bureau. How would she tell visitors the following things?

1. The post office is beside the restaurant.

____

2. The lake is far from the city.

____

3. We're on César Chávez Street.

____

4. The movie theater? It's over there.

____

5. The library is above the Museum of Anthropology.

____

Nombre ______________________ Clase ______________ Fecha ______________

VOCABULARIO Place names *Pupil's Edition, p. 239*

7 Write where you can buy the following things. Then find the places in the puzzle that follows.

1. unos zapatos nuevos ______________________
2. unas flores ______________________
3. un kilo de manzanas: en la tienda de ______________________
4. pan dulce ______________________
5. una caja de chocolates ______________________
6. unos aretes y un collar ______________________
7. un pastel de fresa ______________________
8. un juego de mesa ______________________

T I E X D A D O A B I N X
B E X V E M R C H E D L P
Q M A F N D J O Y E R Í A
M D N L I A C M A D V F S
A U S O S K A E M K J R T
M L M R E H N S O P U A E
A C E E M L K T U A G N L
W E H R O I A I I N U K E
P R C Í U A R B T A E I R
A Í I A F G H L U D T E Í
J A H Á I É Ü E R E E B A
N O R A D Í Ñ S R R R Ñ Z
Z A P A T E R Í A Í Í T Y
D I C H E M Ú R Y A A P B

8 Rodolfo is telling his friend Alejandra about his errands for today. Read about his day and fill in the blanks with the names of the places where he is going.

Primero voy a la **(1)** ______________ para comprar un poco de pan. Después voy a la **(2)** ______________ para comprar unas zapatillas de tenis nuevas. Luego debo ir a la **(3)** ______________ por un regalo para mi hermanito Paquito que tiene cinco años. A las cuatro voy a encontrar a mi mamá y nosotros vamos a la **(4)** ______________ para comprar un pastel. Mañana es el cumpleaños de mi padre. Después voy a la **(5)** ______________ para comprar comida.

Nombre ______________________ Clase ____________ Fecha ____________

SEGUNDO PASO

To comment on clothes, you'll need to know the names of clothing items. You'll also need to use the verb **ser** to describe what things are made of and how to make comparisons.

VOCABULARIO Clothing *Pupil's Edition, p. 242*

9 What would you wear in the following situations or places?

1. un picnic en el parque ______________________
2. el cine ______________________
3. el teatro para ver la obra *Hamlet* ______________________
4. la playa ______________________
5. para trabajar en el jardín ______________________

10 The following people have a certain amount of money to spend on clothes. Write what each person might buy to spend all of his or her money.

MODELO Loni tiene $25; quiere ir a un baile. **Loni va a comprar una falda y una camiseta.**

1. Trini tiene $45; quiere ir a un concierto de rock.
____
2. Gus tiene $30; quiere nadar en la piscina de una amiga.
____
3. Eva tiene $40; quiere comprar unas cosas para ir a la escuela.
____
4. Marcos tiene $60; quiere ir de camping en las montañas.
____
5. Olivia tiene $40; quiere jugar al voleibol en la playa.
____

Nota Gramatical — The verb ser — *Pupil's Edition, p. 243*

To say what something is made of or looks like, use the following formula:
es / son + de + *material* or *pattern*.

La camisa **es de algodón.** *The shirt is (made of) cotton.*
La falda **es de rayas.** *The skirt is striped.*
Los pantalones **son de seda.** *The pants are (made of) silk.*

11 Ernestina works as a salesperson at a local clothing store. How would she describe the following clothes to her customers?

MODELO estas botas / cuero **Estas botas son de cuero.**

1. este traje / lana
____
2. estas faldas / seda
____
3. este suéter / algodón
____
4. esas camisas / algodón
____
5. ese traje de baño / rayas
____

12 Monique is shopping for school clothes. Read her questions and then write the salesperson's response.

MODELO — ¿De qué es esta falda? *(wool)*
— **La falda es de lana.**

1. — ¿De qué es esta blusa? *(silk)*
— ______________________________________
2. — ¿De qué son los calcetines? *(wool)*
— ______________________________________
3. — ¿De qué es el vestido de rayas, señora? *(cotton)*
— ______________________________________
4. — ¿De qué es el traje azul? *(silk)*
— ______________________________________
5. — ¿De qué son estas sandalias? *(leather)*
— ______________________________________

Nombre ______________________ Clase ____________ Fecha ____________

Gramática Making comparisons *Pupil's Edition, p. 245*

- To make comparisons with adjectives, use the following formulas:

más + adjective + **que**	*more... than*
menos + adjective + **que**	*less... than*
tan + adjective + **como**	*as... as*

- The adjective agrees in both number and gender with the noun it modifies.

La falda es más larga que los pantalones cortos.
The skirt is longer than the shorts.

Las sandalias son menos caras que los zapatos.
The sandals are less expensive than the shoes.

La camiseta anaranjada es tan bonita como la camiseta azul.
The orange T-shirt is as pretty as the blue tee-shirt.

13 Read the following descriptions. Then write a statement that compares the two items.

1. La chaqueta gris cuesta *(costs)* diez dólares. Los pantalones verdes cuestan quince dólares.
____
2. Las manzanas cuestan siete dólares. Las uvas cuestan cinco dólares.
____
3. La temperatura del agua en la piscina es de 60º. La temperatura del lago es de 60º.
____
4. La pizza es de 40 centímetros de diámetro. El pastel es de 20 centímetros de diámetro.
____

14 Compare the numbered items and those in Column B by using **más... que, menos... que,** or **tan...como** and the adjectives in Column A. Be sure to use each comparison at least once.

COLUMN A	COLUMN B
bonito	los bluejeans
caro	las botas de cuero
feo	los pantalones cortos
cómodo	una falda de rayas
formal	una camisa vieja

1. La camisa de algodón ______________________
2. La blusa de seda ______________________
3. Las sandalias de cuero ______________________
4. La chaqueta de lana ______________________
5. Los pantalones de cuadros ______________________

Nombre ______________________ Clase ____________ Fecha ____________

TERCER PASO

To express preferences, you'll need to use demonstrative adjectives. To ask about paying for something, you'll need to refer to prices.

Nota Gramatical   Demonstrative adjectives   *Pupil's Edition, p. 247*

- Use the demonstrative adjectives **este, esta,** *(this)* **estos,** and **estas** *(these)* to point out people or objects that are near you.

  Me gusta **esta** falda, pero no me gustan **estos** calcetines.

- Use the adjectives **ese, esa,** *(that)* **esos,** and **esas** *(those)* to point out people or objects that are far from you.

  No me gusta **esa** blusa, pero me gustan **esos** pantalones.

15 Zeena and Charlotte are trying on clothes. Complete their statements with the correct demonstrative adjectives according to the clues in parentheses.

ZEENA: (1) ____________ *(that)* camisa es de algodón, ¿no? Prefiero cosas de algodón. ¿Qué piensas de (2) ____________ *(these)* pantalones?

CHARLOTTE: ¿Ya no tienes (3) ____________ *(those)* pantalones en casa?

ZEENA: Tengo unos pantalones muy similares. Hmm, (4) ____________ *(these)* sandalias son muy cómodas. ¿Qué piensas tú?

CHARLOTTE: No hacen juego con *(match)* (5) ____________ *(that)* blusa. La blusa es demasiado formal.

16 Nicolás is shopping for school clothes with his father. He doesn't like what his father has picked out and prefers some other things he sees in the store. Write what he would say about the following things using the correct demonstrative adjectives.

MODELO botas pardas / botas negras
No me gustan estas botas pardas. Prefiero esas botas negras.

1. suéter de lana / suéter de algodón

   ____

2. chaqueta de cuero / chaqueta de mezclilla *(denim)*

   ____

3. camisa de rayas / camisa de cuadros

   ____

4. pantalones anaranjados / pantalones verdes

   ____

ASÍ SE DICE Asking about prices and paying for something *Pupil's Edition, p. 248*

17 How would you ask how much the following items cost?

MODELO that tie **¿Cuánto cuesta esa corbata?**

1. these socks

¿____?

2. those pieces of candy

¿____?

3. that board game

¿____?

4. this skirt

¿____?

18 Look at the following items and write a sentence telling how much they cost.

1. disco compacto $15 ______________________________

2. camisa $20 ______________________________

3. pantalones $25 ______________________________

4. flores $18 ______________________________

VOCABULARIO Expressions related to cost *Pupil's Edition, p. 248*

19 Abel is buying a gift for his dad. Write what he might say in reacting to these items.

MODELO una falda de lana / $15 **¡Qué barato!**

1. unos calcetines que cuestan $50

____

2. unos bluejeans que cuestan $5

____

3. una camiseta que cuesta $100

____

4. un suéter que cuesta $5

____

5. un cinturón que cuesta $180

____

6. una corbata que cuesta $75

____

Nombre ____________________ Clase __________ Fecha __________

10 Celebraciones

PRIMER PASO

To talk about what you're doing right now and to ask for and give an opinion, you'll need to use the present progressive. You may also need to know the names of important holidays.

VOCABULARIO Holidays *Pupil's Edition, p. 261*

1 Look at the circled days on the following calendar pages and write the name of the holiday associated with each circled day in the blanks below. Then, list at least two things that you associate with each holiday.

1. enero

l	m	mie	j	v	s	d
(1)	2	3	4	5	6	7
8	9	10	11	12	13	14
15	16	17	18	19	20	21
22	23	24	25	26	27	28
29	30	31				

2. febrero

l	m	mie	j	v	s	d
			1	2	3	4
5	6	7	8	9	10	11
12	13	(14)	15	16	17	18
19	20	21	22	23	24	25
26	27	28				

3. abril

l	m	mie	j	v	s	d
			1	2	3	4
5	6	7	8	9	10	11
12	13	14	15	16	17	(18)
19	20	21	22	23	24	25
26	27	28	29	30		

4. mayo

l	m	mie	j	v	s	d
					1	2
3	4	5	6	7	8	(9)
10	11	12	13	14	15	16
17	18	19	20	21	22	23
24	25	26	27	28	29	30
31						

5. junio

l	m	mie	j	v	s	d
	1	2	3	4	5	6
7	8	9	10	11	12	13
14	15	16	17	18	19	(20)
21	22	23	24	25	26	27
28	29	30				

6. julio

l	m	mie	j	v	s	d
			1	2	3	(4)
5	6	7	8	9	10	11
12	13	14	15	16	17	18
19	20	21	22	23	24	25
26	27	28	29	30	31	

7. noviembre

l	m	mie	j	v	s	d
						1
2	3	4	5	6	7	8
9	10	11	12	13	14	15
16	17	18	19	20	21	22
23	24	25	(26)	27	28	29
30						

8., 9., 10. diciembre

l	m	mie	j	v	s	d
	1	2	3	4	5	6
7	8	9	10	11	12	13
14	15	16	17	18	19	20
21	22	23	(24)	(25)	26	27
28	29	30	(31)			

1. ______________________________
2. ______________________________
3. ______________________________
4. ______________________________
5. ______________________________
6. ______________________________
7. ______________________________
8. ______________________________
9. ______________________________
10. ______________________________

Gramática Present progressive *Pupil's Edition, p. 263*

- The present progressive tells what someone is doing right now.
  Felicia **está** decor**ando** el cuarto. *Felicia is decorating the room.*
- To form the present progressive, use the following formula:
  the present tense of **estar** + *present participle*
- For -**ar** verbs, the *present participle* is formed by dropping the -**ar** ending from the verb and adding -**ando** to the stem.
  Estamos limpi**ando** la cocina.
- For -**er** and -**ir** verbs, drop the ending and add -**iendo**.
  Felipe está beb**iendo** un vaso de agua. Mónica está escrib**iendo** una carta.
- When the stem of -**er** or -**ir** verbs ends in a vowel, -**iendo** changes to -**yendo**.
  Estoy le**yendo** el periódico.

2 Change the following verbs to the present progressive.

MODELO (tú) escuchar **estás escuchando**

1. (ellas) dar ______________ ______________
2. (tú) beber ______________ ______________
3. (yo) bailar ______________ ______________
4. (él) tomar ______________ ______________
5. (usted) traer ______________ ______________
6. (ella) leer ______________ ______________
7. (nosotros) estudiar ______________ ______________
8. (ustedes) comer ______________ ______________

3 Anita is at the mall with her friends. Fill in the blanks with the correct present progressive form of the verbs in parentheses to say what she and her friends are doing right now.

1. María Luisa ______________ ______________ (comprar) una falda negra.
2. Santiago ______________ ______________ (ver) una película.
3. Inés y María ______________ ______________ (buscar) unos bluejeans.
4. Nosotros ______________ ______________ (hablar) con unos amigos.
5. Tú ______________ ______________ (escuchar) unos discos compactos.
6. Yo ______________ ______________ (mirar) unos carteles.
7. Bruno ______________ ______________ (leer) una revista nueva.

4 Choose the correct infinitive and form sentences about what these people are doing right now.

MODELO Bo / (comprar, escuchar) / botas **Bo está comprando unas botas.**

1. Marilú / (cantar, buscar) / sandalias y una camiseta para el picnic
____.
2. Rosalía y Nora / (mirar, cenar) / ropa elegante para la fiesta
____.
3. Yo / (escuchar, comprar) / un suéter de lana
____.
4. Tú / (buscar, estudiar) / unas sandalias pardas
____.
5. Pablo y yo / (mirar, cenar) / las corbatas de seda
____.

5 Manuel, an exchange student in Japan, is calling his mother to ask what everyone is doing. Write the questions that Manuel asked her.

MANUEL (1) ¿ ____?

MAMÁ Bueno, tu papá y yo estamos mirando la televisión.

MANUEL (2) ¿ ____?

MAMÁ Melissa está leyendo en su cuarto.

MANUEL (3) ¿ ____?

MAMÁ Creo que ella está leyendo una biografía.

6 Match the phrases from the two boxes to make complete sentences. Use the present progressive to say what the following people may be doing now.

Andre Agassi y Pete Sampras Cindy Crawford y Linda Evangelista Gloria Estefan Maya Angelou el grupo R.E.M.	cantar canciones en español escribir canciones en inglés jugar al tenis escribir poemas muy buenos llevar ropa a la última moda

1. ____
2. ____
3. ____
4. ____
5. ____

SEGUNDO PASO

To ask for help and respond to requests, you'll need to use informal commands and some specific holiday vocabulary.

VOCABULARIO Holiday words *Pupil's Edition, p. 266*

7 Rearrange the items from the word bank into the three categories that follow.

mandar las invitaciones
inflar los globos
colgar las decoraciones
recibir regalos
comprar las bebidas
bailar
llamar a los invitados
decorar la casa
hacer una lista de los invitados
tocar música
abrir los regalos
preparar la comida

Lo que haces...

dos semanas antes de la fiesta	inmediatamente antes de la fiesta	durante la fiesta
______________	______________	______________
______________	______________	______________
______________	______________	______________
______________	______________	______________

8 Leila is preparing for a surprise party for a friend. Based on the chart, write sentences telling what everyone is doing to help. Use the present progressive.

	Yo	Mi hermana y yo	Samara	Jorge	Las hermanas de Samara	tú
inflar los globos					X	
decorar la casa	X					
colgar las decoraciones		X				
llamar a los invitados			X			
comprar regalos				X		
preparar la comida						X

MODELO **Jorge está comprando los regalos.**

1. ______________
2. ______________
3. ______________
4. ______________
5. ______________

Nota Gramatical Informal commands *Pupil's Edition, p. 268*

- Use informal commands with people you address as **tú**, such as friends or family.
- To form regular informal commands, take the **tú** form of the verb and drop the **-s**.

escuchar	→	escuchas	→	**escucha**	¡**Escucha** a la profesora!
comer	→	comes	→	**come**	¡**Come** más frutas y menos carne!
escribir	→	escribes	→	**escribe**	¡**Escribe** las respuestas en la pizarra!

9 Your 100-year-old grandmother is giving you advice on how to live a healthy life. Complete her suggestions using informal command forms of the verbs in the word box.

practicar trabajar descansar cenar caminar comer desayunar

1. ______ muchas legumbres y frutas.
2. ______ los fines de semana. Pasa el rato con amigos.
3. ______ un deporte. Es buen ejercicio.
4. ______ todas las mañanas.
5. ______ media hora todos los días.
6. ______ bien, pero no pases todo tu tiempo en la oficina.

10 You're the chairperson of the decorations committee for the homecoming dance at your school. Create sentences with the correct informal commands to tell each committee member what to do to prepare the cafeteria for the dance.

1. limpiar la cafetería ______
2. sacar la basura ______
3. inflar los globos ______
4. abrir las ventanas ______
5. colgar las decoraciones ______
6. tocar la música ______
7. decorar las mesas ______
8. preparar la comida ______
9. comprar las bebidas ______
10. traer los discos ______

Nota Gramatical Irregular informal commands *Pupil's Edition, p. 268*

Some verbs have irregular informal command forms:

hacer → **haz** ir → **ve** irse → **vete**
poner → **pon** venir → **ven**

11 Rogelio's mother left him a note asking him to run some errands for her. Fill in the blanks in her note with the correct informal commands.

Rogelio,

(1) ______________ (ir) al Supermercado Pagapoco y
(2) ______________ (comprar) las manzanas y las naranjas que están en venta. (3) ______________ (traer) todas las frutas a casa. Luego,
(4) ______________ (leer) la receta para ensalada de fruta y
(5) ______________ (poner) los ingredientes en la mesa. Después,
(6) ______________ (hacer) tu tarea y (7) ______________ (ayudar) a Lily con su tarea.

12 Oscar's friends are giving him advice about how to be a better student. Rewrite their statements, changing the underlined elements to informal commands.

MODELO Debes hacer una lista de toda tu tarea cada día.
Haz una lista de toda tu tarea cada día.

1. Debes poner todos tus papeles para las clases en una carpeta.
____
2. Es importante hacer toda la tarea cada noche.
____
3. Tienes que ir a tus clases temprano todos los días.
____
4. Es importante ir con tus amigos a la piscina a nadar.
____
5. Tienes que venir a mi casa para estudiar conmigo este sábado.
____
6. Debes hacer ejercicio tres veces por semana.
____

Nombre ______________________ Clase ____________ Fecha ____________

TERCER PASO

To talk about past events, you'll need to use the preterite tense. You'll also need to use some expressions related to the past.

Nota Gramatical The preterite *Pupil's Edition, p. 271*

- The preterite tense is used to talk about events completed in the past. For regular **-ar** verbs, the endings are as follows:

yo cant**é**	nosotros cant**amos**
tú cant**aste**	vosotros cantasteis
él / ella / usted cant**ó**	ellos / ellas / ustedes cant**aron**

- Notice the accent mark on the **él / ella / usted** forms of the verbs. The preterite verb form **cantó** will not sound the same as the present verb form **canto.**

13 Keith is talking about what he and his friends did yesterday. Write the correct preterite form of the verb in each blank.

1. Anoche mi prima Luna ______________ (empezar) su viaje a Marruecos.
2. Mis amigas Alicia y Nasrin ______________ (tomar) una clase de yoga.
3. Mi hermana Lupe y yo no ______________ (visitar) a mi abuela ayer.
4. Tú ______________ (escuchar) el nuevo disco compacto de Carlos Vives.
5. Yo ______________ (regresar) a casa muy temprano de mi trabajo.
6. Ayer los chicos ______________ (bailar) en una fiesta muy divertida.

14 For the following sentences, choose the best verb. Then write the present tense in the first blank of the sentence and the preterite tense in the second blank.

tomar llamar estudiar cantar hablar mirar llegar regresar

1. Éric siempre ______________ en el coro de mi iglesia, pero ayer no ______________.
2. Silvia y Elena ______________ español en su oficina, pero ayer ______________ inglés todo el día.
3. Yo casi siempre ______________ en la biblioteca, pero ayer ______________ en el parque.
4. Normalmente tú me ______________ a las seis en punto, pero ayer no me ______________ hasta las ocho.

15 Mrs. Hernández is asking her children what they've done to get ready for their trip to Brazil. Write the questions Mrs. Hernández asked based on her children's responses.

1. —¿ ____?
   —Sí, ya compré los boletos *(tickets)* para toda la familia.
2. —¿ ____?
   —Sí, Eugenio y Ronaldo llamaron al aeropuerto sobre el vuelo *(the flight)*.
3. —¿ ____?
   —Sí, nosotros miramos el mapa de la ciudad de San Pablo.
4. —¿ ____?
   —Sí, Mamá, tú dejaste los pasaportes aquí en la mesa. ¡Estamos listos!

VOCABULARIO Past expressions *Pupil's Edition, p. 271*

16 On Sunday, June 16, 1999, Andrea celebrated her **quinceañera.** During the party, her friends talked about their own parties. Look at the dates they mentioned and fill in the blanks with the appropriate expressions from the word box.

el año pasado **el verano pasado** **anteayer** **ayer** **el sábado pasado**

MODELO Rebeca y Alesia — el 10 de agosto de 1998
Las quinceañeras de Rebeca y Alesia fueron *(were)* el verano pasado.

1. Oralia — el 14 de junio de 1999
   La quinceañera de Oralia fue ______________________.
2. Rosario y Luz — el 15 de junio de 1999
   Las quinceañeras de Rosario y Luz fueron ______________________.
3. Petra — el 10 de abril de 1998
   La quinceañera de Petra fue ______________________.
4. Mercedes — el 8 de junio de 1999
   La quinceañera de Mercedes fue ______________________.

17 Answer the following questions in Spanish.

1. ¿Qué hiciste ayer? ____
   ____
2. ¿Adónde fuiste el sábado pasado? ____
   ____
3. ¿Estudiaste para tu clase de español anteayer? ____
   ____

Nota Gramatical Direct object pronouns *Pupil's Edition, p. 274*

- Direct objects tell us *who* or *what* receives the action of the verb.
- The direct object pronoun can refer to either people or things. It agrees in number and in gender with the direct object it replaces.

  lo = *him, it, you* (formal) **la** = *her, it, you* (formal)
- To avoid repeating a direct object noun, the direct object is often replaced with a direct object pronoun.

  Yo no quiero la sopa. → Yo no **la** quiero.
- The direct object pronoun is placed before the conjugated verb in a sentence.

  —¿Miraste la televisión ayer? —No, no **la** miré.

18 Irene is talking about what she and her friends did last night. Fill in the blanks with the correct direct object pronouns.

1. Tú cantaste esa canción. → Tú ______________ cantaste.
2. Nuru escuchó el disco compacto. → Nuru ______________ escuchó.
3. Ramón y Néstor prepararon la paella. → Ramón y Néstor ______________ prepararon.
4. Nosotros empezamos la tarea. → Nosotros ______________ empezamos.
5. Yo compré esta falda nueva. → Yo ______________ compré.
6. Elizabeth y yo miramos la televisión. → Elizabeth y yo ______________ miramos.
7. Nuria y Salvador tomaron el taxi. → Nuria y Salvador ______________ tomaron.
8. Corey estudió el pretérito. → Corey ______________ estudió.
9. Mildred sacó la basura. → Mildred ______________ sacó.
10. Memo y Lupe lavaron el carro. → Memo y Lupe ______________ lavaron.

19 Carolina and her friends Elisa and Margarita are trying to get ready for a party. Fill in the blanks in their conversation with the correct direct object pronouns.

CAROLINA Ay, ¡qué desastre! ¿Quién tiene mi falda nueva?

MARGARITA Todo está bien. Yo (1) ______________ tengo aquí.

ELISA Oye, Carolina, ¿qué vas a traer a la fiesta? ¿el pastel?

CAROLINA ¡Ay, no! No (2) ______________ compré hoy.

MARGARITA Chica, no hay ningún problema. Podemos ir a la tienda antes de ir a la fiesta.

CAROLINA Vale. ¿Saben dónde está mi camiseta blanca? No (3) ______________ veo.

ELISA ¡Cálmate! Está aquí debajo de la cama. ¿(4) ______________ quieres?

MARGARITA Oye, Carolina, ¡tienes que limpiar tu cuarto! No puedes encontrar nada aquí.

CAROLINA Bueno... eh... ¡ya (5) ______________ limpié ayer!

20 Read the following letter that Leonor wrote to her pen pal. Then, circle the direct objects and answer the questions that follow. *Hint:* There are eleven direct objects.

> *¿Cómo estás? Yo estoy muy bien. ¿Cómo es la vida japonesa? ¿Tienes que ayudar mucho en casa? Yo sí ayudo mucho. Cada mañana hago la cama antes de desayunar con mi familia. Los martes, preparo la cena para mi familia porque mi mamá toma una clase. Los miércoles, mi hermano Davis lava la ropa y yo limpio la cocina. Después de terminar los quehaceres, hacemos la tarea. Cada noche, estudio español y música porque son mis clases favoritas. Tomo una clase de música los jueves por la noche a las cinco y media. Después de la clase, practico la guitarra por una hora.*

MODELO ¿Hace la cama Leonor antes de desayunar con su familia?
Sí, la hace antes de desayunar con su familia.

1. ¿Prepara la cena para su familia los martes?
____
____

2. ¿Toma una clase los martes la madre de Leonor?
____
____

3. ¿Lava la ropa Davis los martes?
____
____

4. ¿Hacen la tarea antes de terminar los quehaceres Leonor y Davis?
____
____

21 Ulrika wants to be sure that everything is ready for her party. Use the checklist to complete the sentences. Use the correct direct object pronoun and verb form for each sentence.

> Jaime—preparar la comida
> Lanie y Floyd—limpiar la casa
> Kevin—hacer el pastel
> Yo—decorar el patio
> Kenesha y Trenell—decorar la sala
> Jody y yo—comprar el helado

MODELO ¿la comida? **La preparó Jaime.**

1. ¿El helado? ______________________
2. ¿La casa? ______________________
3. ¿La sala? ______________________
4. ¿El pastel? ______________________
5. ¿El patio? ______________________

Nombre ______________________ Clase ____________ Fecha ____________

Para vivir bien

PRIMER PASO

To make suggestions and to tell how you're feeling, you'll need to use the verb **sentirse.** You may also want to know the names of some activities.

Nota Gramatical — The verb **sentirse** *Pupil's Edition, p. 291*

Sentirse *(to feel)* is a reflexive, **e → ie** stem-changing verb. Here are its forms:

yo	**me siento**	nosotros	**nos sentimos**
tú	**te sientes**	vosotros	os sentís
él / ella / usted	**se siente**	ellos / ellas / ustedes	**se sienten**

1 It seems no one has been feeling well lately. Fill in the blanks of the following conversation with the correct form of **sentirse.**

ALEJANDRA Ruthven, ¿no (1) ____________ tú bien?

RUTHVEN No, no (2) ____________ bien. No tengo ganas de hacer nada.

ALEJANDRA Lamar no (3) ____________ bien tampoco. No está en clase hoy.

RUTHVEN Rosemary y su hermano Basil tampoco (4) ____________ bien.

ALEJANDRA Nosotros debemos cuidarnos si queremos (5) ____________ mejor.

2 Write sentences in which you describe how the following people are feeling. Be sure to include the correct form of **sentirse** in each sentence, and conjugate the other verbs.

1. Shawna / mal / porque / hacer mal tiempo / hoy

   ____

2. Jeff y Mark / bien / porque / ir a cenar / con su abuela

   ____

3. Ana y yo / no / bien / porque / no / poder / salir / con amigos

   ____

4. Amanda y María / muy contentas / porque / ir / de vacaciones / juntas

   ____

5. Tú / mal / porque / tu amiga / no / va a asistir / a tu fiesta

   ____

6. Yo / magnífico / cuando / mi amiga / llamar / por teléfono

   ____

Nombre ______________________ Clase __________ Fecha __________

VOCABULARIO Keeping fit *Pupil's Edition, p. 292*

3 You and your friends enjoy exercising. Fill in the blanks using the word box with the activities that are part of your friends' exercise routine.

patinar sobre ruedas	hacer yoga	levantar pesas	estirarse

1. Mario prefiere aliviar el estrés con ejercicios orientales. Le gusta practicar el karate y ______________________.
2. Eliseo dice que antes de un concurso gimnástico, siempre debe ______________ bien para evitar daños *(injuries)*.
3. Olivia quiere ser más fuerte. Por eso, va al gimnasio casi todos los días y trata de ______________ cuatro veces por semana.
4. A nosotros nos gustan los ejercicios al aire libre. Por eso, nos encanta ______________ en el parque.

4 Fill in the blanks in the following sports club flyer with the exercises being described.

GIMNASIO ✧ BUENA ✧ VIDA
234 ✧ AVENIDA ✧ ALBACETE
TEL. ✧ 45-52-94

¿Te sientes cansado todo el tiempo? ¿Buscas un lugar distinto para hacer ejercicio? Entonces, ¡el **Gimnasio Buena Vida** es perfecto para ti!

✧ Si quieres (1) ______________, tenemos los mejores instructores del mundo. Todos nuestros instructores estudiaron sus profesiones en Nueva Delhi, India.

✧ Si quieres (2) ______________ sobre ruedas, tenemos senderos muy bonitos donde puedes hacerlo al aire libre.

✧ Si prefieres (3) ______________, tenemos el mejor equipo con todo lo que necesitas para ser más fuerte.

Y no te olvides de (4) ______________, antes y después de hacer cualquier tipo de ejercicio.

SEGUNDO PASO

To talk about moods and physical condition, you'll need to know some appropriate phrases and the names of parts of the body. You might also want to use the verb **doler**.

VOCABULARIO Physical conditions *Pupil's Edition, p. 294*

5 It's flu season and it seems that everyone is sick. Complete each of the statements with the phrase that best describes how each person is feeling.

1. Pablo no se siente bien hoy. ______________ (Está contento, Está triste) porque no puede asistir al concierto de los Gypsy Kings.
2. Ernesto ______________ (está resfriado, está nervioso) porque el doctor dice que va a ponerle una inyección *(shot)*. ¡Tiene miedo de las inyecciones!
3. Lilly ______________ (está triste, tiene tos). Creo que ella es alérgica a mis gatos.
4. Federico ______________ (tiene gripe, está feliz). Tiene tos y, fiebre y no se siente bien.
5. Creo que Lon ______________ (está resfriado, está triste) hoy porque caminó tres millas en la lluvia anoche.
6. Georgia ______________ (está enojada, tiene tos) porque tiene varicela *(chicken pox)* y no puede ir a la fiesta de Anita.
7. Nayana ______________ (tiene tos, tiene fiebre). Su temperatura es de 102°.
8. Sameer ______________ (está preocupado, tiene gripe) porque su abuelo está en el hospital.

6 Fill in the blanks in the dialogue with the correct words from the word box below.

preocupado	triste	tos	nervioso	gripe	resfriado	fiebre

MANOLO Kelsey, ¿qué tienes? ¿Te sientes mal?

KELSEY No sé si estoy **(1)** ______________ o si tengo **(2)** ______________. Primero tengo frío y luego tengo calor. Mi temperatura es de 104°; tengo una **(3)** ______________. Y tengo **(4)** ______________. Casi no puedo respirar.

MANOLO Estoy muy **(5)** ______________ por ti. Debes ir al hospital.

KELSEY ¡No me gustan los hospitales! Siempre estoy **(6)** ______________ cuando hablo con mi doctora. Nunca sé qué decirle.

MANOLO Pero, amiga, debes ir si quieres sentirte mejor.

7 Imagine that you find yourself in the following situations. Write sentences to explain how you feel.

1. Tienes un examen mañana en tu clase de álgebra, pero no pudiste *(you couldn't)* estudiar anoche.

   ____

2. Tienes que cantar una canción para tu escuela, pero te olvidaste de las palabras.

   ____

3. Tu mejor amiga se va para vivir en otro país.

   ____

4. Tu novio(a) te dice que ya no quiere salir contigo.

   ____

5. Tienes una temperatura de 103°.

   ____

VOCABULARIO

Parts of the body *Pupil's Edition, p. 295*

8 Put the following words in the correct categories.

el oído · el pie · el brazo · el estómago · la espalda · la nariz · el ojo · la boca · el pelo · la pierna · los dedos · la garganta

En la cabeza	En la cara
______________	______________
______________	______________
______________	______________

Entre el cuello y la cintura *(waist)*	Entre la cintura y los pies
______________	______________
______________	______________
______________	______________

9 Fill in the blanks with the body parts being described.

1. Tienes diez en las manos y diez en los pies. ______________
2. Las usas para llevar aretes. ______________
3. Debes peinarlo todos los días. ______________
4. La usas para hablar y para comer. ______________
5. Cuando tienes tos, esto te duele. ______________
6. Está entre la cabeza y los hombros *(shoulders)*. ______________

Nota Gramatical doler *Pupil's Edition, p. 296*

- The verb **doler** *(to hurt, to ache)* is an **o → ue** stem-changing verb.
- It is used like the verb **gustar.**

  ¿**Te duelen** los dedos? No, pero **me duele** la pierna.

  Do your fingers hurt? No, but my leg hurts.

10 Max is a nurse in a busy hospital. Complete his statements with the correct forms of the verb **doler.**

1. Señor Farouk, ¿cómo se siente hoy? ¿Todavía le ______________ la pierna?
2. Billy y Leo, ¿les ______________ la garganta hoy? ¿Quieren más helado?
3. Lucita, ¿te ______________ los brazos esta mañana? Voy a darte más hielo.
4. Ay, me ______________ mucho los pies. ¡Y sólo son las dos de la tarde!
5. A los otros enfermeros *(nurses)* y a mí, siempre nos ______________ los pies y las piernas.

11 Can you guess what part of the body has been injured?

MODELO A Tonya le duele tanto que ni puede usar la computadora.
Le duele el brazo.

1. Felix comió demasiado (*ate too much*) para el almuerzo.
____
____
2. Marisa y yo no podemos comer comida muy fría ni comida muy caliente.
____
____
3. Alejo no puede caminar. Tampoco puede llevar los zapatos.
____
____
4. Kirk no quiere ni leer ni mirar la televisión.
____
____
5. Terri no puede llevar sus aretes nuevos.
____
____

TERCER PASO

To tell what you did, you might need to use the preterite of the verb **jugar** and some specific vocabulary. To talk about where you went, you'll need to know the preterite of the verb **ir.**

Nota Gramatical The preterite of **jugar** *Pupil's Edition, p. 300*

Here are the preterite forms of the verb **jugar** *(to play)*:

yo **jugué**	nosotros **jugamos**
tú **jugaste**	vosotros jugasteis
él / ella / usted **jugó**	ellos / ellas / ustedes **jugaron**

12 Fill in the blanks with the preterite forms of **jugar** to tell what Ana and her friends did last summer.

1. Sharmila ______________________ al baloncesto en el gimnasio de su colegio.
2. Adam y Johnny ______________________ al béisbol con sus amigos en el parque.
3. Nosotros ______________________ al voleibol en la playa todos los días.
4. Tú ______________________ al tenis con tus hermanas por la tarde.
5. Mis amigos y yo ______________________ al fútbol americano en el parque.

13 Rewrite the following paragraph using the preterite to tell what these people did last night.

Mis amigos y yo jugamos a muchos deportes. Yo juego al tenis con mi mejor amiga Luisa. Juan y Tagaki juegan al voleibol en el equipo de nuestro colegio. Tagaki juega muy bien. Todos mis amigos juegan al fútbol en el parque después de las clases. ¿Y tú? ¿A qué deporte juegas?

____

____

____

____

____

____

____

____

Nombre ______________________ Clase ____________ Fecha ____________

Nota Gramatical The preterite of **ir** *Pupil's Edition, p. 302*

The verb **ir** *(to go)* is irregular in the preterite. Here are its forms:

yo **fui**	nosotros **fuimos**
tú **fuiste**	vosotros fuisteis
él / ella / usted **fue**	ellos / ellas / ustedes **fueron**

14 Change the verbs in the following sentences to the preterite tense to describe where each person went last night.

1. Yo voy al cine con mis amigos. ______________________
2. Melissa y Éster van al centro comercial. ______________________
3. Mark y yo vamos al concierto de Pearl Jam. ______________________
4. ¿Van ustedes al restaurante Las Mañanitas? ______________________
5. ¿Vas a la librería Cristal? ______________________

15 Cristina and Eloy are talking about where they went last night. Fill in the blanks of their conversation with the correct preterite forms of **ir.**

CRISTINA Oye, Eloy, ¿adónde **(1)** ______________ tú anoche?

ELOY Yo **(2)** ______________ al parque con mi abuelo. Caminamos mucho. Es buen ejercicio. ¿Qué hiciste tú?

CRISTINA Bueno, mis amigas y yo **(3)** ______________ al cine para ver la nueva película argentina, pero llegamos demasiado tarde. Mis amigas **(4)** ______________ a un café para tomar algo, pero yo **(5)** ______________ a casa. ¿Y ustedes?

ELOY Nosotros **(6)** ______________ a la tienda Cómpralo para comprar un regalo para abuelita. Mañana es su cumpleaños.

16 Read what each person bought and then write a sentence telling where she or he went.

MODELO Miranda compró una camiseta azul. **Miranda fue a la tienda de ropa.**

1. Elliot y Sarah compraron unos discos compactos para sus padres.
____
2. Martha y yo compramos unos aretes para llevar a la fiesta de Anita este sábado.
____
3. Conrado compró la nueva novela de Paola Antonia Cabrini.
____
4. Tú compraste unos juguetes para tus primos Lupe y Carlos.
____

Nombre ______________________ Clase ______________ Fecha ______________

VOCABULARIO

Places to practice sports *Pupil's Edition, p. 303*

17 Write the places being described in the blanks provided. Then circle the words in the puzzle.

1. Carl Lewis y Jackie Joyner Kersee deben ir aquí para prepararse. ______________
2. Aquí puedes ver la Copa Mundial. ______________
3. Cuando quiero mirar un buen partido de béisbol, voy a este lugar. ______________
4. Si quieres ver un partido de Gabriela Sabatini, debes ir aquí. ______________

C N O B E N D A K H L Ú H G C O

R A M A D Ñ D R Ú O N R I A K L

M I N S D O T T Y M A M N A W H

Í G R C N E C A M B Y C E A A F

S I Y E H R S L A U H R A S N R

B B I R I A T Z E A T R R I X E

E B H A C R D C D I Ó N E D Ñ S

A Y Y P H R O E X R T E S R C D

B Ñ H R E I T S F T Y J T N K F

S I E W M E E R I Ú C N A E L H

S R O B N E R T K R T O D E S D

E N C I H T A Y L O R B I R I R

A S S T I N A D E N I A O S E R

P I S T A D E C O R R E R L H S

O O I Y T K H Y T H L H T K O R

18 Use the verb **ir** and the phrases in the word box to create sentences saying where the following people went. Then write a second sentence telling what they did there.

la cancha de fútbol	la pista de correr	el estadio	la cancha de tenis

1. Mónica Seles y Martina Hingus ______________________________
   ____
2. Reggie White y Troy Aikman ______________________________
   ____
3. Michael Johnson ______________________________
   ____
4. Los jugadores en la Copa Mundial ______________________________
   ____

Nombre ______________________ Clase ______________ Fecha ______________

Las vacaciones ideales

PRIMER PASO

To talk about what you do and like to do everyday, you might need to know stem-changing verbs. To make plans for your vacation, you'll need to refer to vacation items and use infinitives.

Gramática Stem-changing verbs *Pupil's Edition, p. 318*

- In verbs such as **querer, pensar,** and **empezar,** the letter **e** in the stem changes to **ie** in all forms except the **nosotros** and **vosotros** forms.

  Yo quiero un sándwich de queso. ¿Piensas comer conmigo?

  No queremos ir a un restaurante hoy. Pensamos ir al cine esta noche.

- In verbs such as **poder** and **almorzar,** the letter **o** in the stem changes to **ue** in all except the **nosotros** and **vosotros** forms.

  ¿Puedes ir al concierto de salsa el lunes? ¿Almuerzas antes de ir a tu clase?

  Podemos ir al correo juntos. Almorzamos después de mandar los paquetes.

- Some stem-changing verbs have an irregular **-go** in the **yo** form. These verbs do not have a stem-change in the **yo** form. **Tener** and **venir** are examples of this type of verb:

  ¿Vienes a mi casa hoy? Vengo a mi clase a las ocho en punto.

  ¿Tienes planes esta noche? No tengo tiempo hoy.

1 Some friends are talking about their summer plans. Complete their statements by filling in the blanks with the correct form of the verbs in parentheses.

1. Alicia ______________ (querer) ir a México con su tía Lola.
2. Mis tíos ______________ (empezar) a planear sus vacaciones.
3. Yo ______________ (tener) que ir a Miami para visitar a mis abuelos.
4. Ustedes ______________ (querer) ir a la playa pero no ______________ (poder).
5. Nosotros ______________ (querer) ir al Perú con unos amigos.
6. Tú y tus hermanos ______________ (pensar) trabajar en la tienda, ¿no?
7. Mis primos y yo ______________ (pensar) pasar mucho tiempo juntos este verano.
8. Katerina ______________ (querer) ir a los Juegos Olímpicos, pero no ______________ (tener) una entrada *(a ticket)*.
9. Maurice y Carlos ______________ (pensar) visitar a la familia Suárez en Guam.
10. Mi prima que vive en Alemania ______________ (venir) a mi casa los veranos.

2 Dana and her family are planning to have a party to celebrate a visit from her mother's best friend. Dana is inviting her friend Susana to the party. Complete their dialogue with an appropriate verb from the word box. Some verbs will be used more than once.

almorzar	preferir	querer	empezar
pensar	poder	tener	

DANA Hola, Susana, habla Dana. Oye, mi familia da una fiesta este sábado para la mejor amiga de mi madre. Nosotros (1) ______________ escuchar música y bailar mucho. ¿(2) ______________ venir tú?

SUSANA Sí, claro, yo (3) ______________ ir. Mira, mi hermana Lidia también (4) ______________ venir. ¿(5) ______________ asistir ella?

DANA Por supuesto. ¿(6) ______________ venir tus primos Tomás y Alfredo también?

SUSANA No sé. A veces ellos (7) ______________ que trabajar los sábados.

DANA Bueno, hay mucha comida. La fiesta (8) ______________ a las doce de la tarde y nosotros (9) ______________ a la una.

3 Combine the items below to create questions for Silvia and her friends. Don't forget to conjugate the verbs correctly.

1. Tú / querer / estudiar / conmigo /en la biblioteca

   ¿ ____ ?

2. Ustedes / poder / comprar / refrescos / para la fiesta

   ¿ ____ ?

3. Tú / pensar / mirar / televisión / con tus amigos

   ¿ ____ ?

4. Luke y Renato / venir / a tu casa / para escuchar música

   ¿ ____ ?

5. Nosotros / poder / almorzar / con Lori y Roberto

   ¿ ____ ?

6. Thad y Lorenzo / preferir / salir / con sus amigas

   ¿ ____ ?

7. Berta y Amanda / querer / almorzar / en el parque

   ¿ ____ ?

VOCABULARIO

Vacation items *Pupil's Edition, p. 319*

4 Solve these riddles using the items from the word box.

la chaqueta	la bufanda	el traje de baño
los lentes de sol	las chancletas	
el bloqueador	la cámara	los esquís
la toalla	la maleta	el boleto

1. This will protect your skin from the sun. _______________
2. You need this when you take a trip on an airplane. _______________
3. You put this around your neck to keep warm. _______________
4. Using this will help you remember your trip. _______________
5. You need this to carry your clothes on vacation. _______________
6. You would want to use these if you went to the Alps. _______________
7. These will help you protect your eyes from the sun. _______________
8. You dry yourself with this. _______________
9. You wear this to keep warm on a cool day. _______________

5 Dinh is having a terrible time on her trip and calls Cleo to tell her about it. Fill in the blanks in her statements with the items from the word box in Activity 4.

¡Ay Cleo! No vas a creer lo que me está pasando esta semana. Imagínate, estoy en el aeropuerto y no tengo el **(1)** _______________. ¡Mi padre tuvo que *(had to)* regresar a casa! Luego, llego a San Pedro y descubro que mi **(2)** _______________ está abierta *(is open)*. ¡Y no puedo sacar fotos porque la **(3)** _______________ no funciona *(doesn't work)*! Quiero ir a la playa, pero no tengo ni un **(4)** _______________ ni una **(5)** _______________. Voy a quedarme en mi cuarto toda la semana porque no tengo el **(6)** _______________ y no quiero quemarme del sol. Y tú, ¿cómo estás? Ojalá que mejor que yo...

Nombre ______________________ Clase ____________ Fecha ____________

6 Imagine you've just won an all-expense paid vacation. For each of the following places, list three clothing items you would recommend taking along.

1. Si quieres ir a Puerto Rico, lleva ______________________
2. Si quieres pasar el invierno en los Andes, lleva ______________________
3. Si quieres pasar la primavera en la Argentina, lleva ______________________
4. Si quieres ir a Aspen, Colorado, lleva ______________________

7 Regina and Tonya are going on vacation together, but they didn't pack their bags together. Based on their packing lists, answer the following questions about what they packed.

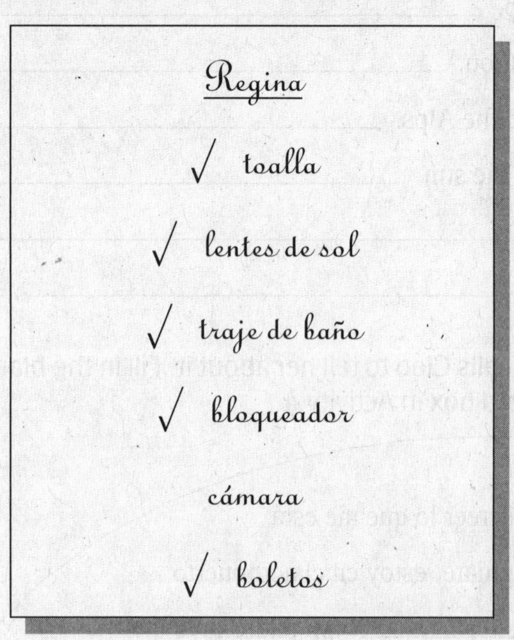

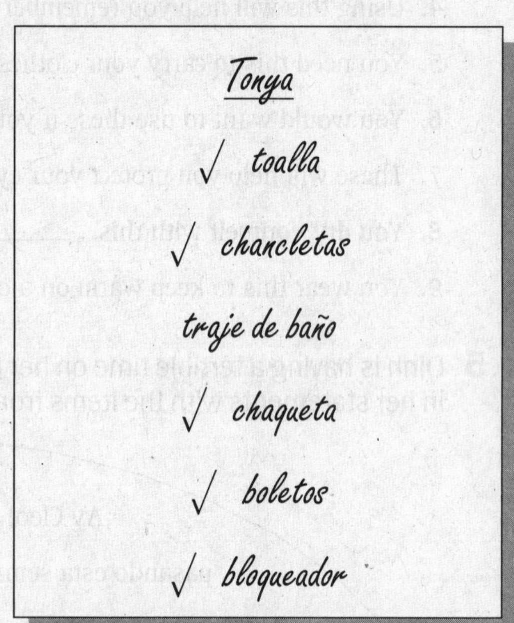

1. Who has already packed a towel? ______________________
2. Who packed a bathing suit? ______________________
3. Who remembered sunscreen? ______________________
4. Who packed a pair of sandals? ______________________
5. Did either of them forget the tickets? ______________________
6. Who is bringing sunglasses? ______________________
7. Who remembered the camera? ______________________
8. What do you suggest Regina take on her trip? ______________________
9. What should Tonya put in her suitcase? ______________________

Nombre ______________________ Clase ____________ Fecha ____________

Gramática Verbs followed by infinitives *Pupil's Edition, p. 319*

- When a verb follows another verb, only the first verb is conjugated. The second verb stays as an infinitive.

  Yo **quiero hablar** con mis amigos. Federico **necesita estudiar** esta noche.

- Some verbs, like **ir** and **tener**, can only be followed by an infinitive if there is another word linking the two verbs.

  Tú **tienes que llamar** a tus padres hoy. **Voy a llamar** a mis padres también.

8 Complete the following sentences about Alison and her friends by using two of the verbs in parentheses. Remember that you'll only need to conjugate one verb.

1. Alison ____________ ____________ su libro de español. (leer, cocinar, necesitar)
2. Nosotros ____________ ____________ a nuestros padres en casa. (comprar, tener que, ayudar)
3. Ustedes ____________ ____________ en el parque el sábado por la mañana. (ir a, esuchar, correr)
4. Yo no ____________ ____________ este verano. No tengo suficiente dinero. (viajar, pensar, estar)
5. ¿Tú ____________ ____________ a la playa conmigo este fin de semana? ¡Excelente! (mirar, ir, poder)

9 Write a negative response to each invitation combining expressions from each box.

ir a	pensar	necesitar	tener que

jugar al fútbol	comer con mis abuelos	ayudar en casa
ver una película	estudiar	comprar nada
nadar	celebrar el aniversario de mis padres	

1. ¿Quieres ir a la piscina con nosotros este fin de semana?

   ____

2. ¿Puedes ir al cine conmigo el viernes?

   ____

3. ¿Puedes venir al parque para jugar al fútbol con nosotras?

   ____

4. ¿Quieres ir al supermercado conmigo?

   ____

5. ¿Vas al concierto de Garth Brooks?

   ____

10 You overheard a friend talking on the phone. Write what you think the other speaker might have asked, based on your friend's answers.

1. —¿ ____?
—No, no podemos ir al cine contigo hoy.

2. —¿ ____?
—Sí, Elena tiene que estudiar mucho esta noche. Tenemos un examen en la clase de historia.

3. —¿ ____?
—No, Carlos y Enrique no necesitan comprar libros. Ya los tienen.

4. —¿ ____?
—Sí, mis padres esperan viajar a Europa este verano. Quieren celebrar su aniversario allí.

5. —¿ ____?
—No, yo no debo limpiar la cocina hoy. Ya está limpia.

6. —¿ ____?
—Sí, tú me debes llamar esta noche. Te llamé anoche.

7. —¿ ____?
—Sara piensa estudiar en España este verano. Quiere hablar el español muy bien.

8. —¿ ____?
—Sí, tú y tu familia deben comer con mi familia esta noche en el Restaurante Comida Fina.

¿Se te ha olvidado? Weather *Pupil's Edition, p. 140*

11 Match the correct destination to each trip, using the following weather reports.

No hace sol hoy en Quito. Y sí, desafortunadamente, está lloviendo mucho también. Hay aguaceros por todas partes. ¡No se olviden de traer sus paraguas!

Bueno, hoy, los que están de vacaciones en Caracas van a estar muy contentos. Hace mucho calor y todo el mundo va a poder ir a la playa. ¡Diviértanse bien y no se quemen del sol!

En Tierra del Fuego, ¡todo está blanco! Está nevando mucho hoy y la temperatura es de 5˚C.

¡En Lima, siempre hace buen tiempo! Va a hacer buen tiempo hoy como siempre. Se puede disfrutar temperaturas alrededor de 22˚C.

Mala suerte para los que están en Patagonia ahora. Hace frío y este mal tiempo va a continuar por unos días. Tengan paciencia, el tiempo va a cambiar el lunes o el martes.

______	1. Simón should travel here for cold weather.	a. Quito
______	2. Marguerite should travel here for nice weather.	b. Tierra del Fuego
______	3. Taylor should travel here for rainy weather.	c. Lima
______	4. Ismael should travel here for hot weather.	d. Caracas
______	5. Irene should travel here for snow.	e. Patagonia

Nombre _______________ Clase _______________ Fecha _______________

SEGUNDO PASO

To discuss what you would like to do on vacation, you'll need to know vacation activities. You'll also need to know how to use the verbs **ser** and **estar**.

VOCABULARIO Vacation activities *Pupil's Edition, p. 322*

12 María has just taken a job as an agent at a local travel agency. Based on her customers' interests, help María suggest an activity for each customer.

ir de vela
explorar en la selva
saltar en paracaídas
hacer turismo
bajar el río en canoa
dar una caminata por el bosque
escalar montañas
acampar

1. RAMÓN Este año, voy a la playa. ¿Qué puedo hacer?
   MARÍA Bueno, usted puede . . .
   _______________.

2. CLAUDIA Siempre estoy muy ocupado. Me gustaría descansar y relajarme un poco. ¿Adónde puedo ir de vacaciones?
   MARÍA ¿Por qué no va . . .
   _______________?

3. INÉS Me gusta pasar tiempo afuera al aire libre. ¿Qué puedo hacer?
   MARÍA Bueno, usted puede . . .
   _______________.

4. MIGUEL Me encanta ver los animales tropicales. ¿Qué debo hacer?
   MARÍA Usted debe . . .
   _______________.

5. JUAN A mi esposo y yo nos gustan los lugares muy altos. ¿Qué podemos hacer?
   MARÍA Bueno, ustedes pueden . . .
   _______________.

6. ROBERTO A mis hermanas les encantan las plantas de todo tipo. ¿Qué pueden hacer?
   MARÍA Bueno, ellas pueden . . .
   _______________.

7. JOSÉ Me gusta pasar el rato cerca del agua. ¿Qué puedo hacer?
   MARÍA Bueno, usted puede . . .
   _______________.

Gramática ser and estar *Pupil's Edition, p. 325*

- **Ser** is used in the following ways:
  1. to say what someone is like — Viv **es** muy simpática.
  2. to say where someone or something is from — **Somos** de Maracaibo, Venezuela.
  3. to define something or someone — Tadita **es** mi mejor amiga.
  4. to say what something is made of — El cinturón **es** de cuero.
  5. to give the date or the time — **Son** las ocho.
- **Estar** is used in the following ways:
  1. to talk about states and conditions — Kristen **está** preocupada.
  2. to talk about location — Daniel **está** en la oficina.

13 Complete Myrtle's postcard to her friend Esther Maude with the correct forms of **ser** or **estar**.

Aquí (1) ______ nosotros en Luquillo. ¡Este lugar (2) ______ magnífico! La playa (3) ______ la más bella del mundo. Yo no (4) ______ aburrida para nada. Hay mucho que hacer aquí. Hoy Trulia y Walter (5) ______ aprendiendo a ir de vela. Bueno, (6) ______ las dos y yo (7) ______ cansada. ¡Saludos a todos!

14 Complete the following dialogue with the correct forms of **ser** or **estar**.

ALECCA ¡Roberto! ¿No (1) ______ listo? Debemos (2) ______ en la fiesta a las ocho.

ROBERTO Es que todavía (3) ______ buscando mi ropa.

ALECCA ¡Ay, Roberto! ¡Tú (4) ______ un desastre!

ROBERTO ¿Por qué no me ayudas a encontrar mi corbata favorita? (5) ______ azul.

ALECCA ¿(6) ______ de algodón?

ROBERTO No, de seda.

ALECCA No la encuentro. Mira, ya (7) ______ las siete. Lleva otra corbata.

15 Several of the following students are studying abroad this year. Use the following elements to describe where each student is from and where he or she will be studying.

MODELO Lucila / San Antonio / Venezuela
Lucila es de San Antonio pero ahora está en Venezuela.

1. Sammy y Jeannie / Raleigh / el Ecuador
   ____
2. Dorotea y Cristina / Denver / Panamá
   ____
3. Vivian y Mario / Cleveland / el Uruguay
   ____
4. Kate / Tampa / Costa Rica
   ____
5. Tomás y yo / Nueva York / España
   ____
6. Abdul / Chicago / la República Dominicana
   ____
7. Daniel / San Diego / Colombia
   ____
8. Diana / Dubuque / la Argentina
   ____

16 Fill in the blanks with the correct form of **ser** or **estar.**

1. Sofía y su hermano ______________ en Buenos Aires.
2. Nosotros ______________ dominicanos.
3. Manuel ______________ triste porque no fue al cine con Pilar.
4. Su oficina ______________ en la calle San Pedro.
5. La cancha de fútbol ______________ cerca del Estadio Municipal.
6. ¿______________ usted profesora de español?
7. Jesse ______________ muy atlética, pero ______________ enferma hoy y no puede jugar al voleibol.
8. La Iglesia Santo Domingo ______________ cerca del restaurante cubano.
9. ¿______________ ustedes de Brasil?
10. Lo siento, señor. La línea ______________ ocupada.
11. Ignacio y Federico ______________ muy cansados.
12. ¿Cómo ______________ tú? ¿No te sientes bien?

TERCER PASO

Gramática The preterite *Pupil's Edition, p. 327*

- To talk about events in the past, use the preterite tense. For regular -**ar** verbs, the endings are as follows:

yo habl**é**	nosotros habl**amos**
tú habl**aste**	vosotros hablasteis
él / ella / usted habl**ó**	ellos / ellas / ustedes habl**aron**

- The verb **ir** is conjugated in the preterite as follows:

yo **fui**	nosotros **fuimos**
tú **fuiste**	vosotros fuisteis
él / ella / usted **fue**	ellos / ellas / ustedes **fueron**

17 Kevin is talking about what he and his friends did yesterday. Fill in each blank with the correct preterite form of the verb in parentheses.

1. Anoche mi prima Luna ______ (empezar) su viaje a Marruecos.
2. Mis amigas Adrianne y Nasrin ______ (acampar) en una isla.
3. Mi hermana Maisie y yo no ______ (visitar) a nuestra abuela el verano pasado. Vamos a visitarla este verano.
4. Tú ______ (explorar) en la selva de Brasil el año pasado, ¿no?
5. Yo ______ (saltar) en paracaídas con mi hermano la semana pasada.

18 Addie has written a letter to her friend Warren about her trip to México. Fill in the blanks with the correct preterite forms of the verbs in parentheses.

¡Hola! Nosotros (1) ______ (llegar) a la Ciudad de México la semana pasada. El lunes Iris y yo (2) ______ (ir) al Museo de Antropología. Después, mis hermanas y yo (3) ______ (visitar) el Parque de Chapultepec. Yo (4) ______ (comprar) unos regalos para todos mis amigos. Ayer mamá nos (5) ______ (llevar) a Teotihuacán. Allí yo (6) ______ (escalar) la Pirámide del Sol. Iris (7) ______ (tomar) muchas fotos de nosotros.

Nombre ____________________ Clase ____________ Fecha ____________

VOCABULARIO

Countries *Pupil's Edition, p. 328*

19 Isabela is telling where she and her friends are going this summer. Complete her statements with the correct country names.

Italia	Alemania	Egipto	Francia	China	Inglaterra

1. Sebastián y Carlos van a ____________________. Esperan ver a la reina Elisabeth.
2. Mateo va a ____________________ para escalar montañas en los Alpes.
3. Lucila y sus padres van a ____________________ para hacer turismo en la ciudad de Beijing. También quieren ver la Gran Muralla.
4. Maricela va a ____________________ para ver la Torre Eiffel. También quiere ver el Centro Pompidou.
5. Yo voy a ____________________ para explorar las pirámides.
6. Claudia y Teresa van a ____________________. Quieren aprender a hablar italiano.

20 Bruce is looking at the monitor in the airport to see when his flight is leaving. Look at the monitor and answer the questions that follow with the correct *country* name.

PEKÍN	10:05 A.M.
BERLÍN	11:30 A.M.
EL CAIRO	12:10 P.M.
PARÍS	1:45 P.M.
LONDRES	2:15 P.M.
ROMA	3:00 P.M.

MODELO Mi madre sale a las tres. ¿Adónde va a viajar? **A Italia.**

1. Mi vuelo *(flight)* sale a las diez y cinco. ¿Adónde voy?
   ____
2. Mi hermana va a salir a las doce y diez. ¿Adónde va ella?
   ____
3. Mis abuelos salen a las dos y cuarto hoy. ¿Adónde van ellos?
   ____
4. Mi amigo Ahmed sale a las once y media. ¿Adónde va él?
   ____
5. María y Anita salen a las dos menos cuarto. ¿Adónde van?
   ____